THE LOG OF

THE GRIFFIN

RHEINFELDEN,
THE NETS IN
THE RAPIDS.

THE LOG OF THE GRIFFIN

THE STORY OF A CRUISE FROM THE ALPS TO THE THAMES BY DONALD MAXWELL. WITH ILLUSTRATIONS BY THE AUTHOR AND COTTINGTON TAYLOR ❧ ❧

JOHN LANE: THE BODLEY HEAD
LONDON & NEW YORK, MDCCCCV

WILLIAM CLOWES AND SONS, LTD., LONDON AND BECCLES

TO

MY FRIEND

JOHANN ALFRED KURATLE

AT ONE TIME PRINCIPAL OF THE
REALSCHULE IN THE VILLAGE OF
NECKER, WITHOUT WHOSE VALUABLE
ASSISTANCE AND ADVICE THE BUILD-
ING OF THE *GRIFFIN* IN THE HEART
OF THE TOGGENBURG COULD NEVER
HAVE BEEN BEGUN

LIST OF CHAPTERS

11

List of Chapters

LIST OF ILLUSTRATIONS

SKETCHES IN COLOUR

13   *b*

List of Illustrations

14

List of Illustrations

BLACK AND WHITE

15

List of Illustrations

16

List of Illustrations

List of Illustrations

List of Illustrations

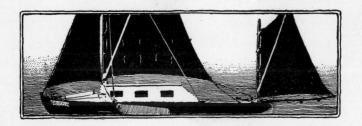

LIST OF MAPS

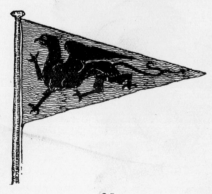

PRO-LOG

IN the year of our Lord one thousand nine hundred and one, when autumn's bronze heralded approaching winter, and the peasant had turned his attention from the hillside to his orchard and cider-press, the good people of the Toggenburg were toiling and spinning, eating and drinking, marrying and being given in marriage, very much as were their fathers before them since the days of Winkelried.

Indeed, so exactly did they fit into Nature, with their generous-gabled houses covered with wooden scales burnt brown or black by successive summer scorchings, their quaint dress and their old-time customs, that they seemed as much a part of the established order of things as the rock-strewn river gleaming among the apple trees, or Sentis looking down on the pine-clad walls of the Neckerthal.

An archæologist would have no need to explore their villages for historic remains, in order to restore to the world a picture of Toggenburg life in past centuries ; for the life of the people in the month of October, 1901, it has been already stated, was almost an exact replica of that of the days of their ancestors.

At this time, however, the above-mentioned

23

orthodox routine was suddenly broken ; for one little village, although over twenty miles from navigable water, had, without any previous warning, burst into boat-building.

The outward and visible signs of this new industry at first had been few. True, Frau Jäger's sewing-machine at the Grütli, Necker, had been pressed into service for the purpose of stitching together lengths of sail-cloth. Certain mysteries in sheet iron were being fashioned at the blacksmith's hard by, and strange shapes were marked out in chalk upon the floor of Herr Wirth's workshop at Brunnadern, the like of which had never been seen by the oldest inhabitant of the district. True, also, from Degersheim to Lichtensteig, from Mogelsberg to Peterzell, the subject of boat-construction had been a constant topic of conversation in Gasthaus and Wirthschaft. But this departure had not changed the face of the countryside or the appearance of a single village. The sun still rose each morning over Sentis, and set at his appointed hour behind the pines of Wasserfluh.

If at this time a stranger had wandered into the Toggenburg, he would have beheld hills indeed, deep blue set with emerald, villages russet and white hiding among orchards, here and there even a glimpse of distant snow ; but, save for two stony streams, no water.

What, then, of this legend of the ship ? At many wayside inns in Necker or Brunnadern a score

of narrators would have told the story somewhat as
follows :—

An Englishman had some months previously
taken up his abode among them. He was, of course,
eccentric—all English are—he had come with the
avowed intention of studying the scenery, but many
of his actions had certainly been extraordinary, and,
some maintained, exceedingly suspicious. Had he
not attended the *Schutzengesellschaft* * meetings and
afterwards sent packages of notes and drawings to
London ? Who knows that these did not reach the
Lord Chamberlain, or Sir Henry Campbell, or Mr.
Bannerman ? Or, again, had he not been known to
cast spells over children, and tap their toes one after
another with a paint brush, muttering to himself the
fateful words beginning " Pig-a-marktt ! " and ending with the curse, " Pleeski-Meesum," when he
arrived at the little toe ?

And had not these eccentricities been entirely
eclipsed by the announcement of his intention to
return home by boat ? This wild project at first
had not been taken seriously, as the nearest point
to Lake Zürich was some twenty odd miles away,
with the Riken to be crossed.

Nevertheless, the boat had been built at Brunnadern. Sages of the village had reasoned with him in
vain. No logic, however brilliant, could check his
insane preparations. After some weeks he had

* Every district in Switzerland has a club (Schutzengesellschaft)
which meets for rifle practice at the ranges.

actually disappeared over the hills with the *Griffin*—for such was the name of the craft—mounted triumphantly on a waggon drawn by two sturdy steeds. News had reached them from Zürich, Rheinfelden, and Strassburg that the adventurer was still alive, but soon he seemed to have been lost sight of altogether, and Toggenburgers had again resumed the routine of their ancestors.

This side of the affair could, it has been said, have been gathered from the people of Necker. The rest can be extracted from the Englishman's note-book, which, for the sake of dignity, is hereinafter referred to as "The Log of the *Griffin*."

THE LOG

I

DER ENGLÄNDER

Aug. 20*th, Necker.*—The time-honoured custom with regard to ships and log-books has been first to build the ship and then to provide her captain with a log-book, wherein he is required by the Merchant Shipping Act to record " conduct of crew, deaths, births, and marriages, sale of deceased seamen's effects, and collisions." But the assumption here evidently is that there will be more than one man on board. In the prospective voyage of the *Griffin*, however, the captain is to be alone : therefore, even if " death " be substituted for " deaths," there will be no one to make the record should this entry be necessary. "Births and marriages" might be dismissed, together with "deceased seamen's effects and conduct of crew;" and there only remains "collisions." In the event of one of these occurring, there would be no further need of the Log at all. And when it states later on that the whole thing is invalid unless signed by the mate, it is not surprising to find that the captain, being forced to depart so much from seamanlike ways, instead of building the ship and then proceeding to the log, defies all nautical precedent by making the log the *raison d'être* of the ship. In fact, no sooner has the *Griffin* passed from a mere idea to a tangible possibility than the log is actually begun, and this entry is made before a single rib of the boat has been fashioned.

For many years the captain has had it in his mind to start from England in a sailing craft, and explore some of the smaller rivers which flow into the Rhine in the district of the Schwarzwald. This, he knows, is quite possible. He can get towed by various tugs as far as Kehl, which is the port of Strassburg. He asks the schoolmaster if it is possible to get up into Switzerland *viâ* the Rhine and Limmat. "No," he replies; "you could not do it. The force of the stream in these rivers is tremendous throughout their whole course, to say nothing of dangerous rapids. You would have to bring your boat from Basle—the Rhine-Rhone

canal will take you there from Strassburg—but
you might be able to *get back* by water." This
gives the captain an idea. Why go to the trouble of
bringing a boat hundreds of miles overland? Why
not, in fact, build one here and navigate her to
England? It would be within the bounds of possibility to have it made in one of these Toggenburg
villages, and then carted over the Riken Pass to Lake
Zürich. The objection that Toggenburgers have
never built a craft before is a slight one, for this will
be so different from any they can have seen that a
preconceived knowledge of lake boat-building might
even prove a hindrance.

No sooner has he turned over this scheme in his
mind than he begins to make inquiries which result
in his ascertaining the possibility of reaching the
Rhine from Lake Zürich by means of the river
Limmat, if he takes the boat through the town of
Zürich and embarks one mile further down. A
craft, therefore, that is to do this journey, must be
built with the following requirements :—

1. Not less than twenty feet in length. A boat
shorter than this would be unreliable in going down
the rapids.

2. Enormous strength. It is necessary to have
a hull that will stand being hurled on to a rock and
off again, without staving in or springing a leak.
There are several places on the Upper Rhine pre-
senting difficulties to which the open part of
Teddington Weir would be a trifle.

3. Decked over, except the well, which must be constructed with a bulkhead, so that in the event of water sweeping over the whole boat, none could get forward of this. Thus, although dragging in the stern, she would still be perfectly buoyant and manageable.

4. Slight weight, although of sufficient strength. Thus, something must be given up in the beam measurements. Nothing can be taken off the length. This is absolutely necessary, for this valley is twenty miles from Lake Zürich, and there is the Riken to be crossed.

5. Sufficient cover to keep several days' provisions, and room to live in. It may often be that some days will be passed in succession without any opportunity of landing.

6. Simply rigged, so that everything can be controlled easily and quickly by one man.

7. Flat-bottomed. It is clearly impossible to have a keel, because many places on the Rhine and Limmat are very shallow. A centre-board is out of the question, on account of its taking up all the room in the tiny cabin. Lee-boards are therefore necessary.

Aug. 21*st, Necker.* — To-morrow morning the schoolmaster has promised to accompany the captain to Brunnadern, a village one mile from here, where the plans of the *Griffin* will be laid before Wirth und Sohn, the local firm of carpenters. The blacksmith

SENTIS FROM THE SOUTH.

The Toggenburg

is also to be present at the conference, for there is no small amount of iron work to be made.

It might be as well for the benefit of the Board of Trade and others to explain where Brunnadern *is*, so that when the *Griffin* arrives in the Thames, if she does, it will be possible to give a clear account of the port of her departure—the Customs men at

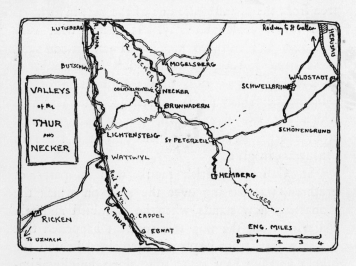

Gravesend probably not being very used to seeing ships flying the flag of the Swiss Republic.

The Toggenburg, formed by the two valleys of Thur and the Necker, is in Eastern Switzerland, not far from the borders of Austria, and is the district lying between the town of St. Gallen and the upper end of Lake Zürich. The whole of this is almost un-known to the English traveller, and the Neckerthal is particularly primitive, inasmuch as no railway has ventured thither, and the "post" is the only conveyance obtainable.

To explore this region, it is necessary to make first for St. Gallen, which, besides Zürich, is the only really important centre easily accessible, a bright lively town, not overrun by tourists, in fact strangely free from them, and quite one of the best in Switzerland for a prolonged stay. It teems with very vivacious and cultured people. Their patron saint came from Ireland, so that a dull race would be an anomaly. The story of the foundation of the Benedictine Abbey (in the seventh century) around which the city has grown, comes through that strange legendary light which only the lapse of centuries can give.

St. Gallen, an Irish monk, with a party of brethren, was passing over the spot on which the monastery now stands, when he stumbled and fell. Believing from the way this accident happened that it was a sign from heaven, he remained behind the others, and lived for some time alone, building himself a hut. In this he was assisted by a friendly bear, who fetched water for him and materials for his work. This bear occurs in the arms of the town, and in old bas-reliefs and carvings is generally represented as carrying a beam. Afterwards St. Gallen built the monastery, which became one of the greatest centres of learning in Europe, though it is to be presumed that he and the faithful bear

ST. GALLEN
CATHEDRAL.

Primitive Travelling

obtained assistance from the inhabitants of the district.

From St. Gallen the village of Waldstatt is reached by train. Thence the journey to Brunnadern must be continued by the " diligence," or " post."

The postilion cracks his whip, and this old-time vehicle starts at a walking pace, and proceeds slowly

TOTAL IGNORANCE OF THEIR *PATOIS*.

up the straight steep ascent through the village. Sentis rises on the left, a wild, desolate series of grey battlements here and there holding a ledge of snow. At the top of the hill the horses break into a trot, and the rattle and rumble of the wheels, and the jingle of the bells on the harness, seem to ring down the curtain on the modern world, and herald with rude music another and more primitive age.

As the road descends into the valley, appear scattered groups of houses built of pine, a quaint mixture of daintiness and boldness ; for not only are they cunningly covered with little wooden tiles of every shade of brown, or grey, or black, and decked out with window-boxes almost Dutch in their neatness, but gigantic beams support huge eaves and over-hanging gables.

And so through the village of Peterzell, with its old covered bridge, and along the valley beside the little river the post toils noisily along until it reaches the village of Brunnadern.

When the captain arrived at Necker—now some ten weeks ago—there was a mild sensation in the place, for an Englishman is a very rare visitor in these parts. At the Grütli, which is also the local bakehouse and under the same roof as the post-office, he was heartily received, and mine host, a man of Titanic proportions, came out to meet him followed by his wife, a fresh-looking little woman from Appenzell, and Susetta, the " maid of the inn," with whom it is apparently quite usual to shake hands. Two children brought up the rear rather timidly, and in addition, a little girl of some three years was discovered, whose big round eyes peeped out from the lee side of Susetta, where she remained for shelter, not being induced to come out under any pretext, lest the terrible " Englander " should eat her.

Especially during the early part of his stay with

Skittles

these interesting people the captain's total ignorance of their *patois* has naturally led him into situations both amusing and dramatic ; but with assistance from the master of the Realschule * close at hand, and the occasional help of Herr Mettler at the mill, both of whom were interpreters on occasion, he has been generally extricated with safety. One evening the

HEMBERG.

Grütli was extra full, and the skittle alley outside in unusual demand. The captain was induced to go and watch the game. He did not know in the least how to play, so that when a ball was placed in his hand, and every one expected him to step forward and

* In Switzerland the educational course is in four stages. The primary school is the preparation for the Realschule. The Realschule leads on to the Gymnasium. The Gymnasium is the next step to the University.

41

show his skill, he was rather at a loss to know what to do. On calmer reflection since, he is convinced that he did himself an injustice, but he confesses with a blush that his ignorance of this game was so profound (perhaps deepened by nervousness—for he felt that the honour of his country was at stake) that he could not remember whether it consisted in steering the ball between the rows of men or in knocking them all down. If he had been asked at any other time he would have certainly leaned to the knocking-down theory, but the man who had played just before had sent the ball with unerring precision right through the whole lot, without so much as grazing one, and this feat had been received with loud applause and clinking of glasses by a group of partisans watching the game with great enthusiasm.*

This decided the captain, and in dead silence he stepped forward to imitate the stroke by aiming carefully in between the figures. Somehow, he miscalculated the weight of the ball, which rolled slowly down the alley, and, to his dismay, threatened to stop before arriving at the other end at all. Its course, too, seemed to change, and instead of going where the captain had intended it should, it just touched the middle figure, and then glancing off to another, stopped dead. The two fell over, and in

---

* The captain afterwards found that the cheering was ironical and derisive, as by this player's failure to score, the party whom they backed had won the day.

their turn knocked down two more, which rolled against others, till they were all laid low. Vociferous cheering rent the air, and a cry of " Der Engländer ! Der Engländer ! " was taken up on all sides. Suddenly realizing the situation, the captain gave a slight bow and beat a quick retreat before any further play might reveal the truth. This happened many weeks ago, but his reputation as a great English " Sport Man," made in that hour, has remained untarnished.

II

THE BUILDING OF THE SHIP

Brunnadern, Aug. 22nd.—When the captain arrives
at the workshop along with the schoolmaster, he is
introduced to " Wirth und Sohn " in person. But
Jacobli, a four-year-old grandson of the ' head,'
although not as yet officially recognized as a partner
in the firm, is for a time far more in evidence than
any other person present. He begins by shouting
lustily, and running round and round the captain in
a state of excessive exultation, and finally climbs on
him to peep half shyly and half saucily into the folds
of his Norfolk coat, which by this time is regarded

A Miraculous Coat

by the smaller children as possessing almost supernatural powers. Its wearer, indeed, has often been known to produce from mysterious folds and pockets, chocolate mice and other sticky joys at a moment's notice and at the most unexpected times. These wonderful performances have been related from child to child without losing anything in the process, as far as the miraculous is concerned, until his coat is looked upon as no ordinary article of dress. Hardly has Jacobli caught hold of the wonderful jacket when he discovers two chocolate mice tied together by their tails hanging from each of his ears, which astonishing occurrence instantly fills him with awe, and finally sends him off to some quiet corner to investigate the reality of this extraordinary gift.

Now that silence has been restored, a space in the workshop is cleared, and the captain launches forth into an explanation of the work to be done, chalking out on the floor the principal measurements of the boat. Sentence by sentence it is translated by the schoolmaster, and after some two hours' discourse, which is punctuated by a few side explanations to the interpreter, the two men express themselves able to understand all the points necessary in the building of the craft. A further explanation is given to the blacksmith as to the ironwork required, and it is decided that the job shall be begun in the morning.

Sept. 2nd, Brunnadern.—Fortunately, the workshop in which the *Griffin* is being constructed stands some way from the stream, and high enough above its banks to avoid the wreckage caused by the floods. The rain has been almost incessant now for two days, and the Necker has changed from a little stony stream to a raging torrent sweeping all before it. Every minute it is rising, and the dull booming of boulders, as they are hurled and tumbled along the bed of the stream, speaks of a force relentless and terrible. The water is thick with grey-brown mud. Branches of trees, logs of wood, planks, bundles of straw, even such things as ladders and benches, has the river rudely snatched from some village higher up. These are whirled past in an inextricable muddle, sometimes getting caught for a moment in a tree or bush, and then, spinning round and round and bobbing up and down, are carried out of sight.

Evidently whole stacks of logs have been swept into the stream, for hundreds have passed already, and the supply is rather increasing than otherwise. Organized attempts are made to secure these spoils. Men armed each with a long pole, on the end of which is a spike pointing downwards, wade as far as they dare into the water, and, when a log is near enough, bring down the spike and haul in the catch. Should he miss it, there is seldom time for another shot, for his prey is out of reach in a moment. One man has hit on a good place at a sudden bend of the stream, where various things on their way down come very near the bank, and he can run along nearly keeping pace with them, striking again and

again until the spike sticks. Another man has
waded into the water, waist deep, where a back eddy
has taken the force out of the stream. Two friends
are holding him on his feet by a rope, which is tied
under his arms. He is reaping quite a harvest of
logs, although now and then he loses his footing and
has to be hauled out of the torrent half drowned.

A warning shout comes from higher up, and the
" spikers " retreat to the bank, as a full-grown pine-
tree, with all its branches, is hurled down like some
shaggy drowning monster. This is the first. Soon
others follow. Two locked together for a moment
get jammed across the stream, and then give with a
crash. One of these threatens the lower bridge at

Necker, but after striking the middle support swings round and is carried through. The water is still rising, although it has now ceased raining for some hours. Things are getting serious, and the Volunteer Salvage Corps is called out. News has come that a

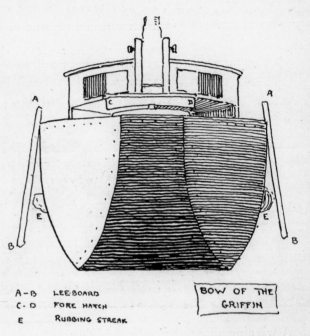

A–B   LEE-BOARD
C–D   FORE HATCH
E   RUBBING STREAK

BOW OF THE GRIFFIN

small bridge at Peterzell has been destroyed, and it is only "touch and go" with the footbridge at Necker. When the evening "post" from Flawil arrives in the twilight, and splashes its way along the flooded road, the water is at the highest point. Before another hour is passed it is going down again

A Deputation

almost as quickly as it had risen before. By the time it is dark every one has had about enough of it. The danger to property is over, and it is by this time not light enough for log-spiking, so the village adjourns to numerous "Wirtschaften" to talk over the day's adventures.

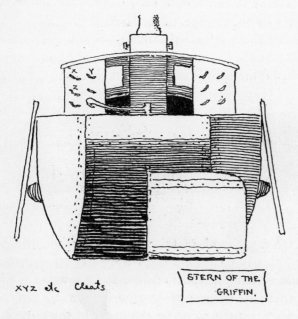

XYZ etc Cleats

STERN OF THE GRIFFIN.

Necker, Sept. 4th.—Whether it was the incident of the skittles that prompted it or not, the captain does not know, but this morning a deputation from the boys of the "Realschule" waits on him to request his active participation in a football match just about to commence. As the thermometer is now standing at eighty degrees [Fahrenheit] in the shade, he is naturally a little astonished. Suppressing, however, any outward sign of his feelings, he accompanies them to the field. The goals are some hundreds of feet further apart than the regulation distance, and "touch" seems to be vaguely defined, chiefly by natural boundaries. The ball is not generally considered out of play until it reaches the Necker stream on one side or the road on the other, or until the players find that they have wandered in fierce dispute out of sight of the goal-posts. The "kick off" is before

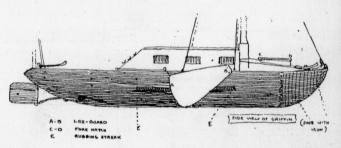

A-B LEE-BOARD
C-D FORE HATCH
E   RUBBING STREAK

SIDE VIEW OF GRIFFIN (SHOD WITH IRON)

two o'clock, and in spite of the scorching August sun, play is continued until five. The Englishman is soon dead beat, but he dare not show this, or his reputation as a great "Sport Man" will be lost, so he goes "goal" for the greater part of the afternoon, and after the game has been hotly contested for two hours and a half, he leaves the field with the school-master, who is captain of the opposing side, both remembering at the same time that they have important engagements to keep. About an hour and a half after this "time" is called.

Summer Football

It appears that when they play football here, the length of the game depends purely on the amount of time at the disposal of the teams. This being only a half holiday, they play all the afternoon. Probably on a whole holiday they would play throughout the day! Possibly some legend of a "three days' match" at the Oval has reached the Toggenburg and it has been taken as applying to football.

In the face of such energy the captain has not the courage to tell them that English teams manage to play

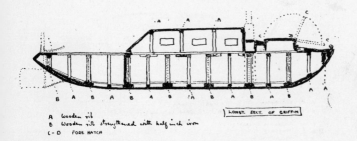

A   Wooden rib
B   Wooden rib strengthened with half inch iron
C – D   FORE HATCH

LONGT. SECT. OF GRIFFIN

only three-quarters of an hour each way on a ground of limited size, and then only in the winter months. It is needless to say they play a hard game and a plucky one. They are fair, too, and in one or two points show style which is surprising, considering that not one of them has seen the game played except among themselves.

Necker, Sept. 5th.—Another deputation. This time it is from the girls. The captain agrees to coach them in the art of football, and a challenge is sent to the boys. The upshot of it is that a match is played in the evening in the small field adjoining the school. The schoolmaster captains the boys' team and the girls are led by the captain, who has to shout directions in English to his fair centre forward (the only member of the team who can understand a word he says), and she translates it into the local *patois*. A good deal of time is lost in this process, and the direction, when finally understood, has often lost its force by a total change of circumstances. Neverthe-

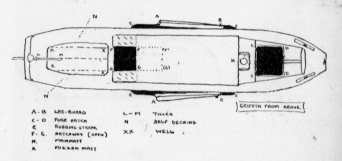

GRIFFIN FROM ABOVE.

A - B	LEE-BOARD	L — M	TILLER
C - D	FORE HATCH	N	HALF DECKING
E	RUBBING STREAK	XX	WELL
F - G	HATCHWAY (OPEN)		
H	MAINMAST		
K	MIZZEN MAST		

less, the boys, utterly taken by surprise at the vigour and order of the attack, are completely routed, in spite of the valiant attempts of their leader, who occasionally gets away with the ball and engages in a terrific single combat with the captain. Meanwhile, both teams face each other, drawn up in line in the Homeric fashion, watching their champions fight it out.

Brunnadern, Sept. 13*th.*—There are two parties. One, consisting of the master of the Realschule and

BRUNNADERN.

A Strange Machine

the men at work on the boat, considers that the Englishman's prospective journey will be difficult and dangerous, but possible. The other, a vast majority, looks upon the idea as preposterous, and certain to end in ignominious failure. But now that the craft has grown in the workshop, and passers-by can see her through the open door, many of the doubters are going over to the other side. At every Wirtschaft it is discussed. One man considers it top-heavy; another maintains (although it is made of wood) that it weighs too much to float. And still another asserts that iron wings are to be fastened on each side, to flap by machinery, and thus propel the vessel!

The captain does not find it easy to make the workmen understand multitudinous details, for all explanations, except when the schoolmaster acts as interpreter, are of necessity made in dumb show, the Toggenburgers and the stranger having no language in common. Sometimes this programme is varied. Whenever boys or girls from the Realschule appear on the scene, they translate the captain's French to the men. Such support greatly expedites matters, and gives him unique opportunities of airing his knowledge of some twenty-seven words of that language, the general meaning of eight or nine of which, after some repetition and with the aid of diagrams, is made clear.

Mogelsberg, Sept. 1 *5th.*—It is impossible to live

any time here and not be struck with the importance of the fountain as a factor in the social intercourse of all these villages. Each one is a focus of activity and a rendezvous for everybody. Here some good Frau coming down to wash her pots and pans, meets a neighbour who is rinsing out linen in a tub, taking advantage of the constant supply of running water. Next comes a man who fills two buckets, and the three stand gossiping for a while. Travellers stop to drink, and children to play. Generally the supply of water, always pure, cool, and delicious, is from a natural spring with force enough to rise to the basin without the need of a pump. Not only are all manner of vessels taken to the fountain to be washed, but the windows of the houses are unhinged and brought down to be cleaned. In fact, it is not much exaggeration to say that these houses are taken to pieces periodically for purposes of cleaning, and half a family may sometimes be seen marching off with various portions of their domicile for a turn under the pump.

Necker, Sept. 22nd.—The mid-day repast at the Grütli is an interesting study. Every one dines at the same table, which is a very long one of oak, scrupulously washed before and after every meal, so that a cloth is unnecessary. At one end sits the landlord, on his right hand his wife and Sopheli, and on his left the two other children. Then come Susetta, the servant, and any workmen that may be

IN THE VILLAGE
OF MOGELSBERG.

The Lee-board Mystery

on the place. To-day there is a strange-looking man with shaggy red hair not unlike a stage pirate, who the schoolmaster explains is a "roof-mender." Then come, in order of social rank, travellers and visitors at the inn, ending up on one side with the schoolmaster. The Englishman is given the place of honour on the other side. Sometimes, however, he is seated at the end, in which case he can see the host, at the other end of an avenue of busy hands, nodding at him in a good-natured way, and, for want of any other means of mutually intelligent expression, raising aloft his glass and pledging him in home-brewed cider, which compliment, to his huge delight, the captain returns in like manner.

Brunnadern, Sept. 24th.—The painting of the *Griffin* has been finished this morning, and nearly everything is complete. The mainsail has been made successfully. The floor of the school house has been used for cutting out the stuff, and a sewing-machine at the Grütli has assisted in getting the different lengths together. The lee-boards have been a great puzzle to the villagers ever since they were made, and a source of wild speculation. It was at first supposed that these had something to do with propelling the boat when becalmed, probably acting as fins. The Englishman was once asked where the engines were going to be placed. The builder, however, gives information on this point, and the problem is more or less solved. The explanation of their use is generally accepted, but it is not considered half so wonderful, and the captain is quite sorry the secret has been let out, for many simple people, who had regarded the *Griffin* as one of the wonders of the world, a sort of steam dragon that would flap sheet-iron wings to order, now begin to look upon her as

A HOUSE IN NECKER.

quite an ordinary boat. This is a reaction, nevertheless, which affects only a few. To the majority, interest in the final details of the craft has grown to fever heat. Now that the "ship" has been brought outside to be rigged, and the unusual sight is seen of

Peace and the Devil

a sail in the roadway over against the fountain at Brunnadern, there is always a small crowd of interested spectators. From early morning until dusk people come to watch the progress of the work, and wise men, who live in the village, and thus are more acquainted with the subject, stand round with looks of profound knowledge, puffing slowly at enormous pipes, ready at any time to explain the working of the " machine " to those less instructed in the marvels of navigation.

Brunnadern, Sept. 28th, sunset.—To-morrow the *Griffin* will be launched at the pond above Furt. The captain, resting from his labours, now that the work is complete, has climbed up the valley side to watch the evening light tinting the Sentis. Everything around is peaceful. The tinkle of a cow-bell and the faint splash of a tiny waterfall are the only sounds that break the stillness of declining day. The eastern sky is cut by the ragged line of Sentis dyed with deepening orange. He is musing on the beauty of the surroundings, and almost lost in reverie, when the calm is rudely broken, and some hundred yards ahead an ink - black figure with lengthy strides and no little clatter dashes across the gold and crimson distance. It is a man in a very Cockney costume, wearing a " topper " and carrying a ladder decorated with sticks and brushes and bags of something black.

A perfect stranger to this district would probably

take the apparition for the "Old Gentleman" himself on urgent business—for does not that ubiquitous personage appear through all the ages in the costume of his time?—but the captain, knowing something of local fashion, remembers that the top hat is never worn in this part, save at funerals, weddings, and other melancholy occasions. Such headgear is reserved (thrice happy Toggenburg!) for the use of chimney-sweeps!

III

THE WONDER OF THE
TOGGENBURG

Brunnadern, Sept. 29th.—At 3 p.m. the *Griffin*
is lashed on a two-horse cart and made ready for the
ceremony of launching, which is to take place at the
pond near Furt. The attempt to get the vessel down
there during the quiet of the afternoon—when it
was thought the children of the villages would be
improving their minds in school—is baffled ; for the
"ship" has hardly started on her overland route
when a cloud of dust proclaims the rapid advance of
many feet in her wake, and it seems to the coarse
Saxon ear of the captain that such a confusion of

voices and mingling of tongues can never have been
equalled since the building of Babel.

Furt, 1 *p.m.*—It is a glorious day for the trial, and
every one seems to have turned out in its honour.
In fact, it has actually been made the occasion for a
public holiday in the district, and along the road from
Brunnadern to Furt, in straggling groups, people are
flocking to see the strange sight of a sail in the
Toggenburg. At Furt a halt is made at the Stag,
which is soon full to overflowing. The captain and
the builders, father and son, sit at a table in the
midst of a jostling crowd. Every one is in the best
of spirits. Numerous are the toasts and speeches, to
which the captain responds with handshakes and
bows, not knowing how else to reply. The schoolmaster of Necker has not yet appeared on the scene ;
until he arrives all hope of mutual comprehension is
vain. Nevertheless, a speech from the Englishman
is insisted upon, and he is dragged to his feet. He
knows that not a sentence will be understood, and
therefore takes care to introduce in his rambling
address a great many names of people and places well
known to his audience. This is just what they want.
Every time mention is made of Brunnadern or the
Toggenburg, he is interrupted by rounds of applause ;
and when he alludes to " Wirth und Sohn " as the
great shipbuilders of the future, deafening cheers and
banging of beer-glasses put a stop to the captain's
eloquence for several minutes. Meanwhile " Wirth

THE SPEECH.

und Sohn," although they have no more idea of what has been said about them than anybody else present, realize that some compliment has been paid to their skill, and look gratified accordingly.

The Englishman's speech continues, when he can make himself heard, with an expression of regret that the master of the Realschule at Necker (loud applause), his friend Herr Kuratle (renewed and prolonged cheering) is unable to be present at this interesting gathering at Furt (cheers). It is therefore impossible for his speech to be translated into the language of the Toggenburg (frantic cheering). He brings his remarks to a close with a patriotic allusion to William Tell, and sits down amidst an enthusiasm that puts all their previous demonstrations into the shade.

After this, the party leaves the inn and proceeds with the *Griffin* up the rough road on the right that leads to the mill pond. This is situated in a very sheltered spot. Even if the few hundred square feet of water were sufficient to try the sailing power of the boat, there will be little chance of getting any wind. Natural steps of grass, not unlike the seats of an amphitheatre, range themselves on one side. Thereon, hundreds of children, chattering in awe-struck and expectant whispers, form a many-coloured back-ground to the *Griffin*, now at the water's edge. The cart on which she is fastened has been backed into the water, and a crowd of well-meaning people, totally ignorant of the subject, are making numerous ludicrous suggestions concerning the method of launching. Every man has a particular method of his own, which he is positive is the nautical one. The captain does not attempt to interfere, for the muddle would probably be much greater if he tried to give them any hints by means of signs, therefore he is quite content to let them get the craft into the water in their own way.

With a very well-directed splash that seems to wet everybody concerned, the *Griffin* takes the water, and a breathless silence follows. When it is seen that she floats right way up, a running fire of comment breaks out, swelling in volume until the whole valley seems to hum with it. One man without delay leaps on to the boat, and stands for a moment on top of the cabin. The *Griffin*, which at present has not an ounce of ballast in her, simply rolls over, tips him into the pond, and rights herself again. He is greeted with shouts of derisive laughter as he is helped out of the water, somewhat surprised.

It is at this point that the captain makes his authority felt, and although he cannot succeed in explaining his wants by ordinary means, signs to them to ballast the boat with stones, with looks of stern command pointing to the surrounding hills and then to the *Griffin*.

His meaning is grasped, after a short discussion amongst themselves, and touching amends are made by tribute of boulders, both great and small, sufficient in quantity to ballast a sailing barge.

THE GRIFFIN
IS LAUNCHED.

The Griffin floats

At last the boat is deep enough in the water and on an even keel, and the noise of many voices gives place to an awe-inspiring silence as the captain steps on board. From the look on the faces of most of the bystanders it is evident that they regard this as an experiment attended with grave risk, and the feeling of suspense could not be deeper if he were going to experiment with fireworks near a powder magazine. Probably the children think the boat will instantly sink, and the captain be drowned before their eyes.

However, nothing dreadful happens. The *Griffin* is pushed off from the shore, and slowly proceeds

DIE CHURFIRSTEN.

round the pond by means of the rudder, which her solitary occupant jerks from side to side. There is no other way of getting along, for sculls have not yet been obtained, and it is useless to set the sail; up to the present there has not been a breath of wind.

After the first round, "Wirth und Sohn" are picked up, and as soon as it is clear there is no danger, everybody wants to come on board. The first load consists of about fifteen people, some crowded in the well, some forward of the mast, and not a few in the cabin. When one crew has had a turn, a struggling crowd is ready to take its place.

The captain is afraid that the boat will be sunk by sheer weight of numbers, so he has to adopt all sorts of strategies to touch the shore where there are fewest people. Although the stream flowing out of the pond is bridged over, where it enters at the upper end it is too deep to wade and too wide to cross by jumping. Thus, although there is a path all along the waterside, it takes some time to get from one side of the stream to the other. The captain resorts to the dodge of heading the boat as if he is going to land on the right bank, and there is a rush to that side. Then he runs the boat up on the left, and takes on board a selection from the less thickly peopled shore. This sort of thing goes on until dusk, when the schoolmaster arrives on the scene, and comes on board also. As night falls this Margate steamer effect gives place to a scene more classical. It brings to mind Virgil's description of restless spirits roaming up and down the banks of the Styx, and crowding round in an attempt to get a place on Charon's barque whenever it should chance to touch the shore.

It is hard work for the captain, but there is one consolation, the Englishman is confident that his name will go down to posterity in these villages along with such pioneers as Galileo and Christopher Columbus. Doubtless, many of the childish onlookers at this afternoon's spectacle, in years to come, when grandchildren climb about their knees, will recount to them the days of shipping in the Toggenburg.

MOGELSBERG.

Pig-a-*marktt!*

This is the last day of the Englishman's stay in the Neckerthal, and numerous little children come running after him, calling "Pig-a-*marktt!*"—which means, for by now it is quite an institution, that he must go through the usual formula with their toes, beginning with the statement that "*that* little pig went to market," following it up with the interesting fact that three others "stayed at home, had

BRUNNADERN.

roast beef" and "had none" respectively, whilst the youngest member of the family cried "Wee, wee, wee, please give *me* some!"—which story, although they none of them know in the least what it means, causes huge satisfaction. This soon gives place to a general romp, and ends up, to their immense delight, with a game in which the captain personates a bear in the skittle alley, very fierce and eager to catch little boys and girls to take them back to England. The schoolmaster comes out to fetch the Englishman in to coffee, and, although there is a twinkle of merriment in his eye, warns him that such unbending will very much lower his dignity and importance in the eyes of the villagers, and advises him, if he romps with the children, to do so in private.

Strange land of contrasts, whose grown-up people cannot play with children, and whose chimney-sweepers wear top hats !

IV

OVER THE RIKEN

On the Road to Lichtensteig, Oct. 1st.—Before the sun has climbed far into the deep blue above, the *Griffin* is on its way up the steep ascent to Wasserfluh. The captain has taken leave of the inhabitants of the place, and after a last hand-shake to the brave, and a last kiss (metaphorical) to the fair, is leaving the Neckerthal for good. Looking back on his stay there, it seems to him like a memory of another age. True, by this time he knows every detail of these villages by heart, and has entered so much into the life of the people that many curious customs, astonishing

77

at first, have become familiar incidents of daily occurrence. True, too, that some have been adopted (in many particulars), and they may even be difficult to throw off when coming again into contact with the outside world. But compared with the routine of life at home, the last few months seem altogether fantastic and unreal, like some fairy story which tells, indeed, of common incidents and ordinary people, yet all the time takes our thoughts into a charmed atmosphere, unconscious of the work-a-day world.

Fantastic, too, seems this journey over the mountains, with a boat rumbling along ahead, its owner unable to make intelligible commands except by means of drawings or pantomimic gestures, helped out occasionally by a few isolated words picked up during the last few months ; stranger still to start out on a cruise of nearly a thousand miles through several countries of whose language the captain is ignorant. Herr Wirth, junior, representing the firm of " Wirth und Sohn," is accompanying the boat as far as Schmerikon, and is seated with the driver on the bow.

It must be borne in mind that the Toggenburg does not have a ship built every day, so the love of display is sure to show itself. The journey, in fact, approaches in character a triumphal procession, and, in spite of advice to the contrary, which being in English is not understood, the driver insists on having the mast up, so that ere long a telegraph wire does its deadly work, and there is a delay of

A TOGGENBURG
GABLE.

several hours while a new spar is being fitted at
Lichtensteig.

Lichtensteig, morning, Oct. 1st.—This is a small
town built on a rocky eminence, rising from the
little river Thur. It consists principally of one
street, out of which curious narrow lanes lead
between houses built up with many goodly beams
and balconies, story upon story, until the sky, whenever a glimpse of it is visible, looks so unusually
far off that the narrow roadway seems to be shut
down in a well. The progress of the boat through
Lichtensteig produces the usual results, people coming
out of their shops and dwellings and staring in
amazement, remaining perfectly still until the phenomenon is lost to sight. The younger generation,
however, not content with this passing view of the
prodigy, come running after, their numbers swelling
as each lane and alley pours out its multi-coloured
tribute of children, to dance behind the cart to
the creaking and rumbling of the *Griffin*, as if it
were indeed the music of the Pied Piper.

Wattwyl.—And so along the dusty road the
procession passes, the crowd growing less and less
as the little town is left behind. A campanile, the
colour of old gold, begins to stand out more and
more from the dark blue background of the Churfirsten peaks, and soon the village of Wattwyl,
through which the stony Thur stream flows, discloses

itself, looking for all the world like a bit of Italy. A fair is in progress, and considerable interest is caused by the sudden appearance of the *Griffin*, but there is comparatively little demonstration, the people evidently taking the captain and his boat for some curious exhibit, and the triumphal passage through the town as part of the show.

On the Road to Uznach.—It is a tedious climb to the bleak village of Riken at the top of the pass, where a halt is made for lunch, and the horses are rested. On the descent towards Uznach an immense tract of country lies spread out ahead. Stretching away towards the west, lake Zürich almost reaches the horizon, and the little lake of Pfaffikon glitters like a jewel in the purple distance. In the south-east the Speer, like a rough-hewn pyramid, seems to rise up from the hillside not half a mile away, although in reality it is ten times as far. At its feet the level country, cut by the tree-bordered Linth canal, stretches away into the mist towards Wesen, dotted with innumerable tall, thin poplars, which at this distance resemble a scattered multitude of people. A small group of wooded hills stands like an oasis in an unbroken plain of green. Then suddenly, out of the mist over against the village of Reichenburg, ramparts and towers of rock rise sheer, crest upon crest, and where snow and cloud are almost indistinguishable, the ice-dragon Glärnisch cuts the sky.

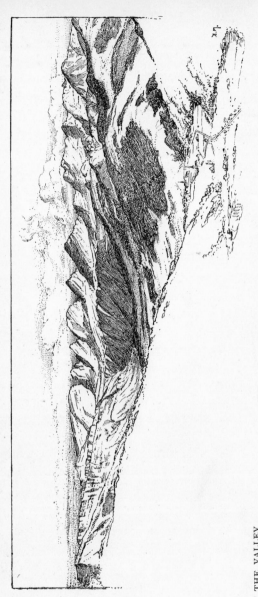

THE VALLEY
OF THE THUR.

The Linth Canal

Such is the view that presents itself to the traveller over the Riken to-day, but the valley did not always look like this. Of its history the following extract from the useful Baedeker is interesting :—

"The *Linth* descends from the valley of Glarus, and often with such violence as to carry large fragments of rock along with it. In process of time these deposits so completely filled the bed of the river that the whole plain between the lakes of Walenstadt and Zürich was inundated, and a once

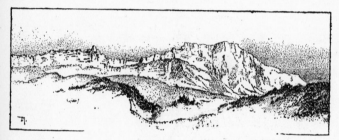

THE SPEER.

fertile district converted into a dismal swamp, from which the inhabitants were at length driven by malaria. In 1807, in accordance with a proposal by *Conrad Escher* of Zürich, the Diet ordered the lower part of the Linth to be converted into a canal, and to be conducted into the Walensee (the Escher Canal), and a new canal (the *Linth Canal*) to be constructed to drain the latter lake into the Lake of Zürich ; or rather, that the *Maag*, an outlet of the Walensee, which formerly flowed into the Linth, should also be converted into a canal. Under

85   E 2

Escher's supervision the works were begun the same year, but not completed until 1822. . . . The proposed object has been perfectly attained ; the land is again under cultivation, and thickly peopled."

Schmerikon, evening.—It has been slowly clouding over all the afternoon, and now the peaks across the valley are disappearing one by one until their individuality is lost and a faint grey mass looming

TOGGENBURG HOUSES.

against the sky takes their place. The air, too, is very chill, and before Uznach has been left far behind a few drops of rain seem to foretell a wet evening. This proves to be a false alarm, happily, for by the time the *Griffin* has reached her destination at the water's edge in the little village of Schmerikon, the setting sun breaks through in the west and floods the landscape with yellow light. The end of the lake divides into a number of channels and lagoons, which run between broad

In the Water

plains of reeds and grasses and rush-covered swamp.
The sunlight, deepening every minute from yellow
into orange, catches on these green expanses, and
throws them into vivid contrast with the back-
ground of confused mountain form, now turned to
a deep purple. Along these shores, and here and
there upon the open water, glide boats, bravely
painted in scarlet, green, and gold, paddled from the
stern like gondolas, each casting an image, line for
line, on the mirror-like surface of the lake.

But there is only a moment in which to watch
this scene, for the *Griffin* is now in the water, and
the captain has to superintend the arrangement of
the ballast. Several sacks are filled with shingle
and stowed in the well. A few more are placed
below, forward of the mast, and, when these have
been properly fastened down, the mainsail is hoisted;
but the air is quite still, not even a shiver stirs it.
The captain, nevertheless, pushes off from the shore
in the hope that a breath of wind may be caught
further out; but this hope proves vain, and he
paddles the boat into the harbour to moor her for
the night. Meanwhile, the men who have been
assisting him divide their attention between the new
craft and a neighbouring *café*; but as it is very cold,
they succumb one by one to the superior charms of
the latter.

The sun has set, and a deep, cold shadow has
crept over everything, except where the cloud-
enveloped heights across the water still flame for a

time. Then the warmth dies out of them also, and sheets of mist the colour of ashes begin to form, and move slowly across the lower hills. A shudder seems to run through the air. Soon the surface of the lake, ruffled for a moment, is quite still again. It is growing colder. Then the captain remembers that he has had nothing to eat since the morning, so he yields also to the attractions of the *café* before mentioned.

The *Griffin* naturally does not cause the surprise to the people of Schmerikon that it has done among the Toggenburgers. The rig is a novelty here, and lee-boards are of course unknown in these waters, which have few shallows and no tides. But to them the only really extraordinary feature about the boat is her prospective voyage to England. This is being discussed when the captain enters the *café*, and he sees that they have already taken sides in the matter. One party is hotly maintaining that the journey is possible, while the other as violently contends that it is not.

After supper, the captain arranges to meet the builder at breakfast (the driver and his team have been gone some time on their way home), and returns to the boat, where he is determined to spend the night. It is certainly not a prospect to be looked forward to with enthusiasm, but later on he will often be obliged to sleep on board, probably in much worse circumstances, so it is just as well for him to begin to harden himself from the first. The

UZNACH.

An Improvised Bed

wind has got up suddenly, and the pale green twilight in the west is darkened by ragged clouds hurrying across the sky. In fact, it looks as if there were some nasty weather ahead.

He crawls into the diminutive cabin, and lights a candle. The wood of the boat has not yet had time to swell, and he notices with some misgivings that a great deal of water has collected already under the floor-boards. This does not augur well for a quiet night, for should it come in at this rate there will be several inches in the morning, or else he will have to bale the boat at intervals. Neither of these alternatives is comforting to reflect upon. He proceeds to improvise some kind of bed with the slender material at his command. This consists of a macintosh and a portmanteau filled with miscellaneous clothing. It is done in this way. The portmanteau is emptied of its contents, making a splendid basis for a pillow made up of a linen sun-hat, three or four ties, and a cloth cap, which are stuffed under a large silk handkerchief. The next thing is to tie up the bottom of the mackintosh sleeves with string (this is to prevent draught), and use these as receptacles for the feet, pulling up the garment with the back uppermost so that it can be buttoned underneath. To do this is quite an athletic performance, and the exercise it necessitates produces sufficient heat to give a comfortable start to the night's rest. All the remaining articles of dress one by one are carefully stuffed underneath the waterproof, care being taken that the thickest things come on top and the softest underneath, reserving something or other for a night-cap.

Any one who cannot sleep peacefully under this arrangement after a few trials should see his doctor without delay, for assuredly he cannot be in a sound state of health.

Schmerikon, Oct. 2nd, 10 *p.m.*—The sleeper is awakened by the encroaching floods, which have produced a cold sensation in his left knee, and he discovers, on striking a light, a small lake on the starboard side, wherein are floating two candles, a pencil, a sodden box of matches, and a tin used for baling. To get the place dry again (or, rather, free from water, for it is a mockery to call it dry) takes him nearly a quarter of an hour, and has the effect of rousing him thoroughly. ·

Later.—There is no further interruption until 3 a.m., when he is awakened, this time by cold water slowly dripping on to his face. The steady patter of rain on the cabin top is audible, and evidently some joint has not been effectually stopped. Luckily, it is only at one place that it comes through, and he avoids this by moving everything further aft. This easy change of locality is one of the advantages of the *Griffin* patent bed.

4.30 *a.m.*—The lake on the starboard side before mentioned has grown considerably, and it has commenced splashing unpleasantly, owing to the rocking of the boat. This is caused by a steam barge, just come alongside the quay. Another period of baling is necessary.

5 a.m.—It is just beginning to get light, and the rain has stopped. Out of the harbour, boats, each manned by a party of "navvies" going to work across the lake, are one by one disappearing into the mist over against the Ober Buchberg; this is the only sign of life at present. Along the quay, with its double avenue of pollard trees, are barges loaded

SOME TOGGENBURG CARDS.

with stone, broad in the beam with square bow and square stern, and a single mast amidships, which carries a huge square lug-sail, hoisted whenever it is possible to run before the wind. They never attempt to tack. Whenever there is an unfavourable wind or none at all, the barge is rowed from the stern with huge sculls, which are pushed through the water, and not pulled, so that the rowers can face the bow and use them to steer with. There is a rudder also, for

93

use when under sail. Like a great many other odd-looking craft in different parts of the world, they are built only to suit local conditions, and would be out of place anywhere else.

Schmerikon, morning.—At half-past six the captain, after cleaning up the *Griffin* a bit and re-packing the portmanteau, is having a wash in the ship's bucket. It may be only imagination, but surely ice would be warm compared with the water of Lake Zürich. The sun is up and the sky has cleared, but, judging from the unsettled state of the weather yesterday and last night, it will probably not be fair long.

At a few minutes to seven, Herr Wirth appears.

" Guten Morgen, Herr Markzvell."

" Guten Morgen ! " is the reply.

" Gut geschlafen ? "

The captain has been so successful up to this point of the conversation that he disdains to reply in mere German, but breaking into the *patois* of the Toggenburg, exclaims—

" Yo, yo ! "

He is not, however, proficient enough in the language to add the fact that this sleep was indulged in during very short periods of time, with numerous interruptions and at long intervals.

" Ist viel Wasser im Schiff? " is the next question.

For answer, the captain points to the well of the *Griffin*, which is quite empty, as it has just been, baled. He remembers that this Toggenburger knows nothing of boat-building (except what he has picked up in the last month), and accordingly he would probably not know that a boat first put into water ought to leak. He would be bitterly disappointed if he knew that periodical exertions have been necessary during the night to keep down the floods, and would think it a sign of bad workmanship.

"Das ist gut!" he exclaims.

"Sehr gut," solemnly replies the captain; and they stroll towards the *café* for breakfast.

A BOAT ON LAKE ZÜRICH.

It is, of course, impossible to keep up this fluent conversation for long, and after a mutual "Guten Appetit," the meal proceeds in silence, broken occasionally by an allusion to the weather. The Englishman remembers two German sentences, learnt long ago from a phrase book. One concerns the loan of a snuff-box, which is a difficult theme for discussion, and the other being translated is, "Will you pass the sugar?" If he could only introduce this one it would be splendid; but, alas! the sugar is so awkwardly near—in fact, almost touching his saucer —that he is afraid it will appear a little forced to ask this question. Therefore, attracting the attention of his companion in another direction, he commences slowly pushing it away. He has nearly succeeded in placing it reasonably out of reach, when Herr Wirth, noticing what he takes to be stealthy efforts to obtain it, politely places it within easy access, so that the plot not only fails utterly, but the captain is compelled to load his coffee with an unusual quantity of sugar.

V

ZÜRICHER SEE

Schmerikon to Lachen, Oct. 2nd.—There is a very faint breeze from the direction of Uznach, and the *Griffin*, at 7.45 a.m., moves out of the harbour under mainsail only. It will be risky to carry more canvas with only one on board, for the wind is very treacherous in these waters, and it is quite common in certain states of the atmosphere to be calmed one minute and the next to be taking in sail for dear life and running with bare mast before the squall. Thus everything must be under easy control in case of emergencies, when a moment's unreadiness would be fatal—at least for the boat.

The Log of the Griffin

Herr Wirth comes aboard for about half a mile, and is landed a little way out of Schmerikon, taking leave of the captain with hearty wishes for a "Gute Reise!" He stands some time looking proudly after the craft he has built, which is making a course for the middle of the lake in the hope that the breeze there will be fresher. But when the village is nearly out of sight, the wind dies down altogether, and the *Griffin* remains motionless on a surface unruffled. The sun is blazing, but there is a coppery colour about it that looks suspicious, and there is blue sky where the mountains ought to be.

Hour after hour passes, and there is no change. However, it is by no means unpleasant. It is a relief to be quite alone after having been for some time the centre of a sort of show, and it is not half so formidable to steer a ship through the known dangers of wind and sea as to face the unknown difficulties of a Toggenburg village.

A good opportunity, too, it proves, for drying several articles which suffered from the water last night; these are spread on the roof of the cabin, which by this time is quite hot. It is encouraging to find, also, in baling the boat, that the amount of water getting through is growing perceptibly less. The captain takes his field-glasses and has a look round, although little more than the immediate shore of the lake is visible. Astern, near the entrance to the Linth canal, the square tower of Schloss Grynau is to be seen, and to the right of that the woods of Ober-Buchberg slope down towards the water. Ahead there is a faint group of towers, probably Rapperswyl, and to the left of them stretches a long low shore of swamp land, covered with tall grasses which extend in patches out into the lake. Lachen can just be discerned over this waste, and it

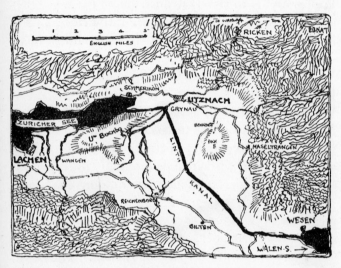

THE LINTH CANAL.

is there that the captain wishes to find shelter, if possible, for the night, by means of an hour or two's paddling.

It is not until the sun has set that the *Griffin* enters the little harbour. It has been very slow work, mile after mile in a dead calm, along the lonely shore, in silence broken only by the

monotonous noise of the paddle or the melancholy
cry of some startled wild-bird.

Lachen, Oct. 3rd.—A glorious morning, bright
sun, cloudless sky and a fresh breeze whipping up
white horses on the dark blue surface of the lake.
Rapperswyl is so clearly defined across the water that
it looks like a town in miniature quite close, and it
is difficult to realize that it is some three miles
distant.

It is perfect weather for sailing, and the captain,
hastened by the fact that it is probably too good to
last, loses no time in breakfasting at a neighbouring
café. The wood of the boat has swollen considerably
by now, and the amount of baling necessary has been
very much less, so that sleep extending over periods
of several hours without interruption has been
possible—which state of things, compared with the
trials of the night at Schmerikon, can only be
described as " bloated luxury."

There is not much to see in Lachen. The charm
of the place lies in its situation, so there is no reason
why a start should not be made at once. It is
difficult to get out of the harbour in the teeth of the
wind, and the *Griffin* fails twice on account of the
entrance being too narrow for going about, and it is
impossible to make the lake on one tack. The
captain therefore takes in sail while he is towed out
by a local waterman. Then, close hauled, heading
towards Pfaffikon, the *Griffin* is under way, pushing

A BARGE ON
LAKE ZÜRICH

her blunt nose noisily through wave after wave, and plunging about so that the boat is drenched from stem to stern, and the captain from head to foot.

She is carrying far too much sail ; for it is blowing harder every minute. But the temptation to try this mountain-built craft against the weather and see what she will stand is too much for the

SCHLOSS GRYNAU.

captain, and he keeps her on her course without taking in a reef.

"Hard a-port ! "

The *Griffin* comes up into the wind, and her sail, wrestling with the mast, flaps with a noise like a volley of musketry. She pitches heavily for a while, sending up sheets of spray, and then, lumbering over on to the other tack, catches the full force of a shrieking squall, and is off again, lying over on her beam ends.

"Cling on to the lee scuppers," shouts the captain, as a wave half swamps the well.

"Haul up that dragging lee-board on the weather side and man the pumps!"

If any one thinks this entry in the log is fanciful, and the shouting to an imaginary crew put in merely for picturesque effect, let him get out in any sailing boat, of any rig whatever, into any open bit of water big enough to have its own way for a few miles, and when he is under a cloudless sky and surrounded by a white-topped sea, with spray to sting him in the face and wind to whistle round his ears, then, if he has no one better to shout to, he will shout to himself, but he must shout.

Using his foot for a belaying pin, round which he fastens the end of the sheet, ready at any moment to slip off if a heavy gust should make it necessary, the captain gets free one hand and manages to bring the ship's bucket into use in reducing the amount of water in the well, for by this time there is enough shipped to cause considerable dragging of the stern.

When this has been accomplished—a task by no means easy—the wind has begun to drop, and within a few minutes it has died down altogether. The change is extraordinary in its suddenness. The sky becomes leaden in colour, the sun assumes that same copper tone that it had yesterday, and the surface of

THE TOWERS OF
RAPPERSWYL.

Becalmed

the lake, though still rough, begins to flatten out into an oily, rolling plain, in which the *Griffin* wallows unceasingly. Her spars, creaking and groaning in melancholy helplessness, fall idly from one side of the boat to the other. This sort of thing goes on for some hours, and this day threatens to pass in very much the same unexciting way as the last. It will probably be impossible to get beyond Rapperswyl before sunset.

A tug with a train of empty barges is making its way towards the stony waste near Lachen, where some excavation is in progress. In the hope that one may pass in the other direction, the captain does not attempt to scull anywhere, but keeps to the middle of the lake near the bridge that crosses to Rapperswyl, through which everything must go, ready to take advantage of the chance of a tow. Meanwhile tea is served, and is a great success, except for the fact that there is nothing with which to boil the kettle (it is afterwards discovered that the kettle has been left behind), and there is no cup of any kind. The difficulty is overcome by rejecting ordinary etiquette in afternoon teas, and drinking beer out of a saucepan, the apparent vulgarity of which act is more than atoned for by the exceeding thinness of the bread and butter.

Lake Zürich, evening (*near Rapperswyl*).—A little island not a quarter of a mile long, covered with trees and very green, serves as an anchorage for the *Griffin*, which has just been cast off a train of barges going down the lake. To the east is the bridge from Pfäffikon, at the other end of which stands Rapperswyl, about a mile away. To the west lies another small island, dark against the twilight sky, and beyond it, at intervals, groups of lights show where towns and villages are scattered along the shore.

Night.—Raining again. It does not seem to be able to settle down for more than a few hours at a time, and it looks as though there is some very bad weather to come.

Supper is a lonely and cheerless meal, and it is well over. Outside, everything is black. There is not a breath of wind, and there is no sound to break the stillness of the night save the rain pattering continually overhead, and no movement but that suggested by the flickering candle throwing weird shadows across the floor of the boat and sending a few stray rays of light to wander among the dark foliage without.

Oct. 4th (near Rapperswyl).—When the captain appears on deck in the early hours of the morning it is to find a rather choppy sea and a strong breeze blowing straight up from Zurich. All hands are piped on deck, sail is set, and the good ship is soon over against the vine-clad eastern shore of the lake. While on the next tack a high wind springs up from the north-east, and for a few minutes the *Griffin* is

RAPPERSWYL.

A Gale

ploughing her way through breakers. Soon it blows a gale, and the captain, unable to keep any sail up, is forced to run back to Richterswyl with bare mast. A dead calm then follows as abruptly as the storm had sprung up.

It is simply extraordinary how quickly the wind will get up and die down again anywhere near mountains. In the late afternoon a fresh breeze has arisen from the north-west. The *Griffin* is across the lake near Meilen within half an hour.

At sunset half a hurricane is blowing, and at times it looks as if every bit of tackle will be carried away. Two steamers are the only craft which have not run in for shelter. Heading up the lake, almost into the wind, steering for the Tower of Thalwyl, still to be discerned in the twilight, the solitary *Griffin* is watched by many from the shore as she pitches heavily in the waves, which occasionally sweep over the cabin and fill the well.

Darkness has fallen by this time, and the lights of the villages are the only indication of land. At last it is impossible to keep up any sail at all, and the *Griffin* runs for shelter behind a small promontory near Meilen, screened somewhat from the wind and sea. Everything promises a safe night.

After some few hours' very troubled sleep, the captain awakes to find himself being banged violently up and down in the boat. Waves are breaking over the cabin, the well is full, and the *Griffin*, broken loose from her moorings, has been driven up on to the rocks. The cause of all this is soon apparent. The wind has shifted round towards the west, and every previous advantage that the place may have had as an anchorage has become a source of danger. The bay is now a lee shore, exposed to the full force of the waves, which roll in with increasing strength on the shallow and stony bank. It is quite impossible to get her off single-handed, and even if help can be obtained, every stitch of canvas will have been carried away.

Another hour—wind and sea still rising. To stay on board seems quite suicidal; to attempt to get ashore equally so. But a choice has to be made, and the captain decides to get help from land, and, if possible, to rescue his sketches and clothes, leaving the boat to be broken up. Exactly how he gets to land he does not clearly know, but, somewhat bruised and scraped, he finds himself scrambling up the stone bank into a vineyard, which borders the road to Meilen. Along this a man, bent to the wind, is approaching, carrying a lantern. A high iron fence divides the vineyard from the road, and, as the captain is unable to scale this, he hails the man in English.

Now, the captain is not at all a bloodthirsty-looking man, and—as far as outward appearances go— would not be readily taken for a highway robber or a pirate chief; but it must be remembered that a weird, hatless, shoeless, coatless figure, gesticulating wildly at dead of night, shouting in a foreign language,

FLIGHT!

amid the howling and shrieking of the winds,
however innocent his intentions, must be an unusual
sight to this good native of Switzerland. He seems
to think so, anyhow, by the way he bolts. No

doubt, he takes the captain for the demon of the
storm calling down imprecations, in some diabolical
language, upon his native land.

Nor does the shipwrecked mariner fare better in

three other attempts to get help. There are a few houses not far from this place, and at none of them can he get any answer to his repeated knocking, doubtless being taken for a drunken man.

After a series of fruitless attempts to attract attention in other ways, he starts off for Meilen, and soon his ear catches the sound of music. On following it up it proves to come from a house adjoining the lake, and as the outer door is open, he unceremoniously enters the room from which the festive sounds proceed.

The next few seconds would be invaluable to a painter of such popular subjects as " Man the lifeboat ! "

A comfortably furnished and well-lighted room, with a cheerful fire in a half-open stove, presents sufficient contrast to the black fury of the hurricane without. Beside a little polished table sit a man and a woman, whilst the third—probably the good man of the house—is performing on some kind of stringed instrument. A gust of wind from the suddenly opened door has blown the music across the room, and with countenances expressing different degrees of astonishment, all three have turned towards the new-comer, who, bare-legged and dripping wet, was endeavouring to commence some form of apology or address. Unlike the man on the road, these people seem to take in the situation at a glance, and in a very few moments cut short the captain's somewhat incoherent oration by producing

Salvage

lanterns and ropes, and setting out under his guidance to the scene of the wreck.

By the time the party reach the vineyard, the *Griffin* has been washed so far up on to the stony shore that it is possible to get on board without

A STONE BARGE.

getting very much drenched. A line from the bank is fastened to the mast, sketches and baggage are landed tolerably dry, and the boat is abandoned.

The salvage party conduct the captain to their house, putting numerous wet garments of his to dry around the stove, and send a deputation with him to the Lion at Meilen, where he soon enters the land of dreams, accompanied by the loud strains of an intensely energetic band, performing half the night at a dance under the same roof.

VI

A FISH OUT OF WATER

Meilen, Oct. 5th, morning.—Wind more moderate,
but still blowing hard from opposite shore. On
every hand are traces of last night's hurricane.
Branches of trees are scattered about in the road, and
many of the shrubs in boxes at the entrance of the
hotel are on their sides in a helpless condition. A
steamer has been wrecked at Rapperswyl and another
found, broken loose from her moorings, drifting
about with no one on board. It is therefore hardly
to be expected that the *Griffin* will be recognizable,
considering the fact that she must have been tossed

up and down on the stony shore all night. Consequently, it is with little hope of ever seeing his boat again—except in separate pieces—that the captain finds his way along the road to the vineyard which was the scene of so much adventure last evening.

Encouraged and surprised at seeing a mast still appearing over the vines, he scales the wall and climbs down to the lake. The *Griffin* has been washed up, half out of the water, and wedged in between two large stones. Her bow seems at first sight to have been badly knocked about. Luckily it is where sheet-iron covers it, and it proves on further inspection, although seriously dinted and devoid of paint, to have sustained no structural damage. The wood of the rudder, where it comes below the iron frame, has been torn off, but this will make little difference. If anything, there was a little too much depth before, and as the ironwork will prevent any further tearing away, it is perhaps on the whole an improvement. One of the lee-boards is somewhat bent. These injuries, together with the loss of nearly all the paint on her hull, seem to be the only changes in the craft since yesterday. The well is full, but very little water has found its way into the cabin. The carpenters of Brunnadern have done their work well indeed.. Any ordinary boat, even one built for strength, would have been matchwood by now, after last night's churning up and down on the rocks. The skin of the *Griffin* is of one-inch planks, each dovetailed to the other with strips of steel. The ribs are two inches thick, and eight of them have three-quarter-inch wrought-iron bars fashioned to fit them all round, so that the hull is a veritable tower of strength against a crushing force from without. Last night has proved this.

The captain calls at the house of his rescuers to thank them for their kindness and apologize for his interruption of their musical evening. He finds it rather difficult to put his sentiments into intelligible form. The part that expresses gratitude is understood at once, but the meaning of his apology for the breaking up of the domestic concert is totally missed. They take it that he is referring to some instrument, and cannot understand what it has to do with the case. Probably they think he would like to hear a tune on the mandoline. Whether this is a correct guess as to their deductions or not, the mandoline that figured in last night's scene is brought out, and the captain is entertained to a song well sung and tolerably well accompanied, of which he shows immense appreciation. He insists on several encores, by this means making up to some extent for inability to express himself clearly, and establishing most friendly relations with the whole household.

New wine and large pears, an extraordinary alliance, are produced by way of refreshment, and the captain is presented with a card on which is inscribed—

Jean Bucher,
Maler,
Meilen,

119

giving his own in exchange and explaining—for his knowledge of a few words of German tells him what "maler" stands for — that he also is a painter. Encouraged by this additional bond of sympathy, his host takes him all round the house, and shows him certain paintings of his own, executed in hours of relaxation from his sterner moments of professional work. The captain makes the moderately truthful statement that he has seldom seen pictures like them, and points out that the wind has now gone down considerably, so that he ought to be starting.

Herr Bucher will not allow him to leave without first making him accept as a present an enormous pear, and he accompanies him to the spot where the unfortunate *Griffin* is stranded. It is a cold task, standing in the shallow water and levering the boat inch by inch further into the lake until she is afloat again.

Lake Zürich, afternoon.—The *Griffin* has now got across the lake, and, under the shadow of the peninsula of Au, a lovely mass of dark rich foliage, relieved by fields and orchards, is keeping close to the weather shore by Horgen. The weather is still wet, cold, and gusty, and even the lower hills have traces of snow upon them.

Enge Harbour (Zürich), evening.—Reached here this evening. This ends the journey as far as the

ZÜRICH.

lake is concerned. This afternoon the *Griffin* left the beautifully situated village of Thalwil in squally weather. It has not improved at all, and is still raining. During the whole time from Schmerikon until to-day the barometer has been unsteady. Hardly a mountain has shown itself, except in an hour or two of extraordinary clearness before a rain storm. The wind has been blowing more or less up the lake every day, so that the *Griffin* has had to beat up continually, but for one occasion, when it veered round enough to cause the wreck at Meilen.

Zürich, October 8th, morning.—Zürich, through which the green Limmat flows, is a lively and sunny town, a quaint mixture of ancient and modern. Electric trams run gaily under the shadow of time-battered buildings. It has a dainty appearance, spread out around the shores of the lake, with two most curious cathedral towers as its leading features.

Here the *Griffin* receives her first check, for the captain finds on inquiry that his previous information concerning the Limmat is totally wrong, and that not only at Zürich, but at several other places there are mills which block the river. There are only two ways of getting through at all. One is to wait until a Sunday, when the mills will not be running. Even then there will be serious obstacles, and there are five days to wait. The other is to have all the mills stopped and compensate them for loss of time, a plan quite feasible to navigators who

are also millionaires.   One solution of the difficulty
is to take the boat by train to Rheinfelden, from
which town there is a clear course.   This advice the
captain decides to take, and he makes arrangements
at the railway goods depôt accordingly.

Zürich.—The *Griffin* is placed on a luggage-
waggon, and starts for the station.   There is the
usual solemn procession through the streets and the
inevitable crowd of onlookers following at a little
distance.   At the goods yard it is found that the
boat is too long to pack.   There is much time spent
in conversation, and it seems that the delay will be
considerable.   At length a party, after hunting about
among innumerable luggage-vans for some time,
returns pushing one that is of the required length.

Rheinfelden, October 6th.—Rheinfelden is a quaint
group of towers and ancient gates rising abruptly
from the wildly surging rapids—one of those little
towns which the world calls " slow," but which to
the painter is like the treasure cave of Aladdin.   A
bridge, covered part of the way with an old and
undulating tiled roof, crosses the river cautiously
like some huge creeping beast that treads, now here,
now there, wherever he can find a footing, and dares
not trust his weight where the swirling waters are
deep and strong.   A hundred feet or so below, on
the Baden shore, is a group of primitive fishing-nets
on long balanced poles, having an almost Oriental

A TOWER OF
RHEINFELDEN.

appearance. The local sytem of fishing is certainly not laborious. One of these nets, weighted with a few stones, is let down into the river. This is periodically pulled up. In the unlikely event of some fish being unfortunate enough to find itself over this part of the stream at that moment, it is caught.

Day and night the water rushes against the massive stonework of the bridge, foaming as it divides. Above, the rapids are even wilder, and the surface of the river is like an estuary, brown with shifting sand and mud, when the wind is struggling against the tide ; only here the waves rear themselves ever in the same place, tossing their heads like chained monsters bewitched.

On the eastern side of Rheinfelden the walls are still complete, and towered gates throwing bold masses against the sky, command the roadways from the country-side. Coming upon them from amongst the trees, for aught else that can be seen, the ancient masonry and crooked roofs give the impression of some old tapestry brought to life, and the feeling of having been spirited back into the past, which some of the older streets convey, would be permanent but for the occasional sight of an arc lamp.

It is the electric lighting that gives the place so curious an aspect at night, for this jumble of old streets under such brilliant illumination seems at first like some very realistic exhibition, and the new-comer finds himself thinking how well it is done.

The Log of the Griffin

And, *apropos* of this subject, why is it that scene painters, when attempting to portray a city in the middle ages—say the fourteenth century—almost invariably make the houses of that period tumbling about in every direction, as if they had been standing for some five hundred years untouched? Did none of the buildings of another period survive, and was the age so rough that, with street fights and one thing and another, a house got so knocked about that before it had been up many years there would hardly be a roof, except of a very decrepit character, or a square foot of plaster without a few red bricks peeping through?

Above the rapids is an electric generating station, where the enormous force of the river is used not only to light the whole district, but also to provide electric power which will drive all the mills for miles round, and at a merely nominal cost. There is a place near here where four circular saws are at work from morning till night, and the cost of the power to keep them going is fourpence per day! This plentifulness and cheapness of electricity will, alas! bring many factories to the district, and thus spoil its old-time charm. Already the mushroom growth of unlovely buildings has begun on the Baden side of the water.

The day has not far advanced when a messenger comes to the hotel where the captain is staying, with the news that a "ship" has arrived at the station. It is not easy to find a way to the river. The banks

RHEINFELDEN.

are steep and high on both sides, and it seems impossible to get anything down to the water at all unless it is lowered from the bridge. Some one suggests the abrupt slope at the side of the brewery on the left bank below the bridge. The captain goes to inspect, and obtains leave to embark there. A cart is therefore dispatched to the station. A small group of people from the hotel, who are "in the know," collect in the grounds of the brewery when

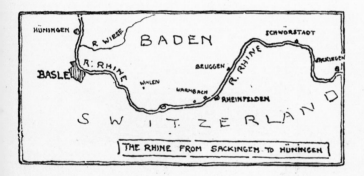

THE RHINE FROM SACKINGEN TO HÜNINGEN

the *Griffin* arrives. Inch by inch she is lowered to the water by ropes. A certain amount of ballast is necessary, although sailing will be quite impossible, and a few sacks are filled with stones. Then the captain bids farewell to the inhabitants of Rheinfelden and jumps on the boat, which is lowered further into the water, still held, however, by several lines.

One by one these are cast off, and the *Griffin*, caught in the swirling waters, is carried away. Its

occupant, paddle in hand, standing in the stern with
the tiller between his knees, is seen for a moment or
two endeavouring to keep the head of the boat down
stream. He glances back for a minute, and catches
a glimpse of the fast receding towers of Rheinfelden
and the little group on the high bank ; then he is
shot out of sight round a bend in the river.

VII

RAPIDS

Rheinfelden to Basle, Oct. 6th, afternoon.—The journey down from Rheinfelden is most exciting. There are sudden drops in the river like irregular weirs, where the water shoots down and rears itself up into a series of steep waves. It is at such places quite impossible to keep a straight course. The *Griffin* turns round and round, and the great thing is to cling on, for whenever she strikes a rock, and this is not infrequent, there is a shock as if a barrel of gunpowder had gone off in the cabin. By the time the water is baled out of the well, after going down one of these rapids, there is sure to be another in sight. They can sometimes be avoided, as they seldom stretch right across the river. Every now and then steering is impossible, and it is wiser sometimes to let the water carry the boat where it will.

When the two rose-coloured spires of the cathedral at Basle come into sight, the captain knows that the old bridge is not far ahead. It is a danger that he has been somewhat dreading. If the *Griffin* can get through *that* without accident, then she need not fear anything on the Rhine, for it is a regular terror, standing as it does on many piers, some of stone and some of wood, against which the river foams, tearing through the more fiercely for being pent up in narrow channels. When near the baths the captain steers the boat to the right bank, which is on the inside of the curve, to take advantage of a slacker current, and puts on all speed possible by paddling. Then, when close to the bridge, he seizes the tiller and aims straight for one of the piers. For a moment this manœuvre seems suicidal, but it is necessary to see which way the current is setting on to the buttress. Then, with the helm hard over, the *Griffin* dodges a few feet off this course, towards the shore side, and shoots the bridge unscathed. A few astonished faces appear over the parapet above and watch her being carried round the bend towards Hüningen. It is an exciting experience, which brings to the captain's mind a picture of the last time he had seen the river here. He remembers, when a little boy,

THE OLD BRIDGE, BASLE.

arriving by train at Klein Basel with his father at
three in the morning. An engine had run off the
line, and the traffic had all been disorganized, so
that the train came in several hours late. When
crossing over the old bridge they had stopped to
rest—for they were carrying bags—and had peered
over into the dark, green, swirling waters below, his
father remarking that there wouldn't be much chance
for a boat down there. This happened more than
fifteen years ago, but the sight of the river again,
rushing through the old bridge, makes it seem like
yesterday.   To-day's adventure forms a strange
sequel.

Hüningen (*two miles below Basle*).—The captain
succeeds in landing on the right bank, and prepares
to get the *Griffin* under the pontoon bridge. He
makes fast a rope to the shore, and then, standing on
the bow, pays it out, and lets the boat drop down
stream. With all the tackle lowered, she has barely
an inch to spare in passing underneath. There is
little danger of the craft being stolen, so the captain
makes his way into Basle in search of a square meal.

Hüningen, night.—About 10 p.m. the captain
returns to the *Griffin*. It is the first night on the
Rhine, and the restless river tearing by contrasts
strangely with the tideless waters of Lake Zürich.
It is cold and cheerless and lonely beyond description. Hour after hour he lies awake, for the boat,

tugging and pulling at her moorings with rhythmical persistency, foams at the bow and swings from side to side incessantly, making melancholy music of a most depressing character. All the time the dull metallic booming of the pontoons, as the river hurls itself against them, makes a roar so Satanic in its weirdness and so terrifying in its suggestion of relentless power, that sleep for a long while is impossible.

At the best of times a night on the water is a liberal education in the matter of noises. The captain, on this occasion, with his ear against the side of the boat, hears some of the most extraordinary sounds that nature or art can produce, a veritable study in gurgles. At one moment it seems that the *Griffin* has sprung a leak, and is sinking rapidly. At another there is a shrill swishing noise as if she is being towed at a fearful pace. Then for a second or two nothing can be heard but the booming of the bridge. Several times during this long watch he scrambles " on deck " in terror at the sudden cessation of this gurgling accompaniment, thinking that he is adrift. On each occasion, nevertheless, he finds the *Griffin* safely moored.

After some hours of such nervous torture he gets off to sleep, only to wake with a start from a dream that the boat had broken loose and was being carried helplessly down on to a pontoon bridge. He looks ahead to make sure that it *was* a dream. Horrors ! he can see nothing. Where is the bridge ? He

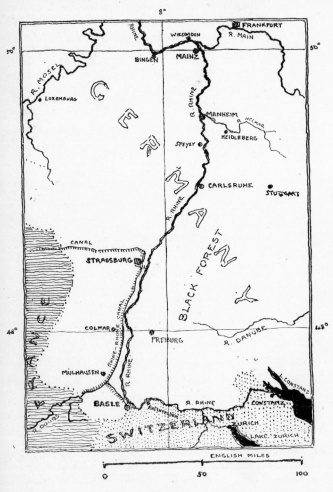

THE RHINE
FROM CONSTANZ
TO BINGEN.

must be adrift in reality this time. But on going forward, he finds the rope sure enough, tugging and pulling, but vanishing into space. Then he realizes that a fog has fallen, and he turns in again. But it is not to sleep.

Hüningen, Oct. 7th.—With the first suspicion of dawn, the captain lands and takes an hour's walk along the bank. When he returns he finds a customs officer on the bridge looking at the strange craft in blank astonishment.

It is a relief to see a human being after so long and lonely a night.

"Guten Morgen," says the captain with an affected carelessness, as if it were a most ordinary thing for him to chat away in German.

"Morgen," grunts the man in reply, eyeing him all over, as if he were addressing a being just dropped down from Mars. He evidently had not thought of him in connection with the mysterious boat.

"Das ist mein Schiff," the captain explains, pointing to the *Griffin*.

The officer gazes hard in the direction indicated, just as though he were looking at a new species of fish with wings, but he says nothing beyond a muttered word that sounds like "Dummkopf."

The situation begins to get strained, so the captain, feeling that he must break the ice somehow, exclaims—

"Ich bin aus Toggenburg gekommen !" He

rather fancies this last effort, but the only effect it produces is to make the officer edge further away.

" Wie weit ist es zu nexten Burglein ? " asks the captain in desperation.

" Verstehe nicht ! " is the only retort.

After this the captain decides to abandon further attempts at conversation, the customs officer evidently being exceedingly dull. Trusting to find a more favourable spot for taking in supplies, he leaps on board, and once more pushes out into the racing current. As he does so, another man joins the officer, and the latter is tapping his head significantly and pointing to the boat of weird design now rapidly disappearing from their view.

Noon.—Another pontoon bridge ahead. The bank happens to be low here, so that landing is simple, or rather comparatively so, for the stream, even against the shore, is running at nearly five miles an hour. There is some delay, for the reason that two inches more are wanted to get the boat under the bridge.

The only solution of the difficulty is to weight the boat so that it lies deeper in the water. A group of onlookers is at once pressed into service, and after a brief explanation of the work to be done— which the captain delivers in fragments of several languages he doesn't know—they proceed to get into the boat. By virtue of their added weight and by dint of much vigorous pushing, the vessel emerges on the other side of the bridge not much the worse for the operation.

3 *p.m.*—Hundreds of islands, covered with thick undergrowth and unending rows of poplars, stretch out on each side as far as eye can see. What villages there are must stand back a long way from this network of tributaries and backwaters.

Judging from glimpses that can be seen from the boat as she rushes by, many of these side streams must be very interesting ; but the want of life around makes the scenery rather dull to the solitary traveller. About every half-mile or so a patch of shingle shows above the water, on which a group of black and exceedingly solemn-looking birds are generally assembled. They watch the *Griffin* as she is swirled nearer and nearer, and then with harsh cries wheel into the air, as if they resent the invasion of their barren kingdom.

The effect of all this is indescribably depressing —mile after mile of the same monotonous scenery. Tens of thousands of poplars stretch away into the distance behind, until they resolve themselves into a grey mist, and ahead exactly the same prospect presents itself.

4.30 *p.m.*—Great event ! Man seen cutting wood on the bank ! Intense excitement on board. Every one crowds on deck. At once the scenery, before so monotonous, looks positively interesting. It is decided to hold converse with the native.

" Guten Morgen ! " shouts the skipper, forgetting in the excitement of the moment that it is now quite late in the afternoon.

The man stops chopping, and looks towards the river with intense surprise written all over his face.

" Das weatherlein ist sehr gut ! " he continues, mustering his best German.

Still no response.

" Comprend sie nicht ? " a distinct doubt entering his mind as to the nationality of the workman, who is still gazing open-mouthed at the boat.

Still no answer.

With an indignant " Sprechen sie Deutsch ? " the captain is carried on until a bend of the river puts all further conversation out of the question.

On, on, in her headlong course rushes the *Griffin*, swept down by the relentless force of the stream, as if she were a leaf or piece of cork. It is impossible to describe the sensation such travelling as this produces, so intermingled are the feelings of unbounded exhilaration and of utter helplessness. The captain gives up all attempt at steering, for it is clear that the caprice of every current must be obeyed. At one time the boat spins round and round. At another she remains in one position for some miles. Occasionally she is caught in a back eddy, and held up for a time in her race downwards.

The overwhelming sense of loneliness caused by the monotony of the banks, together with the excitement of each succeeding moment, have the effect of

THE ASTONISHED
WOODCUTTER.

obliterating all sense of time but the present. It is impossible to reason. There is no thought of rest or refreshment—simply a wild desire to push on and lose no time. There is also no attempt to get food, although nothing has passed the captain's lips since last night. Incredible as it may seem to read in cold blood, he has no sensation of weariness or hunger, nothing but a dull perception of some force urging him to fly down stream.

Sunset.—Another man is in sight. The captain throws off his depression, and hails him to ask if there is such a thing as a Wirtschaft within a mile or so. At the word "Wirtschaft," the man, before somewhat inclined to be lethargic, suddenly becomes filled with astonishing vigour, and shouts "Ja, ja!" pointing with one hand, and beckoning energetically with the other. So swift is the current, however, that by the time the *Griffin* is brought to the shore, she has been carried over a mile down stream, so it is as well to go on.

Later.—It is growing dark, and mist is forming rapidly over the river. Soon only the tops of trees on the banks are visible, and these are disappearing one by one. It is not a comfortable feeling, flying along in a fog, with only a momentary glimpse of some landmark to give a clue as to the position of things. It is clear overhead, and a few stars are showing, but soon everything else has vanished ;

and although the water is seething and swirling on every side, yet for all the progress that can be discerned, the *Griffin* might be at anchor. The captain begins to wonder whether he has been whirled into some quiet backwater, so deceptive is this feeling, until the top of a poplar suddenly shows for a moment over the mist, and he sees in an instant that the boat is tearing down stream, broadside on, as fast as ever.

A sound like the far-off rumble of a train can be heard above the constant seething noise made by the river. The captain leans forward and puts his hand to his ear, listening. Then he springs up in terror, and seizes a paddle. There is no mistake—it is the distant roar of a pontoon bridge !

The danger is a fearful one, for there is no means of telling where the shore lies, owing to the mist which obliterates everything. To make matters worse, the stars, visible a little while ago, have disappeared, and there is nothing to go by except the ominous rumbling, which is growing perceptibly more distinct. The captain throws the paddle into the stern rowlock, and sculls hard with both hands, endeavouring to reach the bank with the *Griffin* on such a course that the sound of the pontoon is away on the starboard side. But this seems an almost impossible task. First on one side, and then on another, at one moment ahead and at the next astern, the roar of the bridge seems to be flying to meet him. The situation has all the horror of a

An Apparition

nightmare, and the captain wishes, for the first time in his life, that he had no friends or relatives. Suddenly, through a rift in the fog, a black mass shows itself in the sky, and rushes over the *Griffin*. What on earth is it? For a moment the captain imagines he must have let his nerves get the better of him. Is it a gigantic " clipper of the clouds " built of iron? Then, in a flash, he perceives that he has been carried under a railway-bridge, and the apparent motion of the sky monster is caused by the headlong flight of the *Griffin* down the river. It remains visible above the fog for a minute, and gives the captain something to steer by.

Crash! The nose of the boat has run up on to the stone bank, and the captain scrambles to the top, paying out rope all the time, and succeeds in making fast the long painter to a tree-stump, after being roughly dragged along the ground for some yards by the *Griffin*, as the river tries to tear her off again.

He sits on the bank for a minute listening to the rush of the waters, and staring stupidly into the fog ahead. One by one his scattered senses begin to come back again, and he discovers that he is hungry. It is now nearly twenty-four hours since his last meal. He also realizes that it is very cold ; but whether it is this that is making him shudder all over, or whether it is merely a reaction from the last half hour, he does not know.

On walking a few paces he comes to a building which proves to be an inn. A ray of orange light streams out of a window, and loses itself in the thick mist. He wonders on entering that the simple folk stare at him open-mouthed. Surely they have seen a man before ! He is not able to get food and lodging until he has blundered through an incomprehensible effort in their mother tongue (which probably did very little), and shown a handful of silver (which probably did a great deal) ; for a wild-looking man with dishevelled hair and strange garments is an object of very natural suspicion, especially when he appears suddenly from nowhere in particular, the earth on his clothes suggesting that he may have grown up suddenly out of the ground.

VIII

THE MAN WITH THE BUNDLE

Alt Breisach, Oct. 8th.—When the captain wakes this morning, it is to find a yellow sun struggling up through the river mist, which is slowly advancing up stream. The lower layers still hang in heavy festoons from bank to bank, but the moving air, catching the higher stratum, has pulled it into a thousand attenuated shapes, and twisted it into fantastic writhing chains of white vapour. Here and there through this shifting veil the course of the boat-bridge can be traced to a point across the Rhine, where a steep jumble of houses, built on an

151

eminence, and crowned by a church with three towers, discloses the position of Alt Breisach.

It is not safe to start until the fog has lifted, and it is eleven o'clock before the *Griffin* is under way.

Limburg, about noon.—Another boat-bridge ahead ! Very steep stone bank. Landing will be no easy task.

The captain has by this time adopted a regular method of getting ashore, which he is beginning to think is rather effective. When approaching a bridge, he brings the *Griffin* within a few feet of the shore, and then ties a long rope round his waist, fastened at the other end to the bow, and passing over the cabin. Then, putting the helm over so that the nose of the boat runs up on to the bank, there is an interval of about two seconds, in which she is swung round by the stream and washed off again backwards. During this interval the captain has to get his footing, and prepare for the tug. He will never quite forget Limburg, because it is here that he is pulled off his feet, and, out of his depth, is towed backwards in the direction of a pontoon bridge. A little hard swimming, however, brings the *Griffin* again within a few yards of the shore, though not until alarmingly near the roaring bridge, when, by suddenly paying out all the slack rope, he manages to scramble up the bank and make fast the painter.

After the boat has started off again from Limburg, the captain changes his clothes, and determines to have a washing-day. First the boat is mopped down, and then a general "wash" is started. Although everything goes off well, somehow the things do not look quite as "clean" things usually do. Happily, he hits on a method of rubbing the collars up and down between rough stones, which system not only gets them clean, but also frays them sufficiently to give them somewhat the appearance of real laundry work. Any chance observer from the bank would have been surprised to behold the mast, bowstay, and shrouds of the *Griffin* made use of as drying-grounds. Not only are garments of every description blowing in the wind, but a whole suit of clothes, recently submerged in the river, is spread out on crossed paddles, and looks not unlike a scarecrow. It is to be hoped that the people in this part of the world are not superstitious, or the sudden appearance of the *Griffin* will be taken as a fearful omen, foretelling famine, pestilence, or death.

Oct. 9th, Ottenheim.—There is a fresh breeze this morning, and although it is blowing dead up stream, the captain determines to use it. He has only one lee-board left, the other having been torn off by a rock yesterday evening, so that the boat makes considerable lee-way while on the starboard tack. It does not matter very much, however, in a river running like this one. The slacking of the current near the banks makes it difficult to get the boat up into the wind. The swifter water catches the stern, and it is generally necessary to ware. It is rather risky work, for the *Griffin*, instead of obeying the current and thus avoiding obstacles, now that she has a motion of her own, several times nearly runs herself on to a shoal, and once is saved from going aground only by the loss of her one remaining lee-board. At last her rudder strikes a rock with such violence that a piece of the bottom of the boat is torn out. In a few seconds the well is full. Were it not for the water-tight division, which separates this from the cabin, the boat would sink in a minute or two. However, except for a dragging in the stern, this makes comparatively little difference to the sailing. The captain puts his feet against the half-decking on the other side, and thus avoids the flood. It is a comfortable position, but hardly a secure one. Every now and then there is a sudden lurch; he slips, and a heavy splash accompanies his involuntary immersion in the well.

10 *a.m.*—The spire of Strassburg is visible. Within twenty minutes the captain has brought the *Griffin* to land at Kehl, on the right bank, and moored her there. It will be necessary to get the boat out of the water, and repair her at once.

Strassburg, 11 *a.m.*—Great news! The captain has called at the post-office, and finds several letters awaiting him. One is from a friend who is taking a holiday in Heidelberg. "Have heard of your

ALT BREISACH.

escapade," he writes. "Do you want a first mate? If so, I will come and sign on at once. Write, and fix time and place for meeting." The captain does not lose two minutes in wiring—

"Boat at Kehl. Meet tow-path 4 o'clock to-day. Wire Kehl."

"That will give him five hours," he says to himself, and he proceeds on his way, feeling that a new epoch has begun in the history of the *Griffin*.

The captain seeks advice from many people in the town, but no one succeeds in understanding his wants. At length he runs across a man who knows a little English. To him the story of the *Griffin* is related in outline, and the necessity of finding some one to repair the boat is made clear. The stranger advises him to call on the president of a well-known rowing club in the town, who will, he is assured, be only too glad to help him out of his difficulty. "He sport man, you sport man," he adds quaintly.

Thanking his informant, the captain makes his way to the Strassburg "Sport Club." The president is a charming man, but with a very limited knowledge of English. His desire to show courtesy to the stranger, by pretending to be satisfied with the captain's German, is so great that he refuses absolutely the services of an interpreter at hand, and, instead, wades through explanations, cross questions and crooked answers, during the greater part of an hour, before understanding the gist of the interview. Eventually the lucid interval of mutual comprehension arrives, and the president offers to "dry dock" the boat in the Club House, which is situated on one of the canals.

Full of gratitude, the captain leaves, and in the afternoon retraces his steps to Kehl. He calls at the post-office, and finds awaiting him a wire from the mate.

"Will meet at Kehl, four," it reads.

The river is only a few minutes' walk, and it has struck four already. The captain is consequently quite prepared to see the mate waiting patiently beside the *Griffin*. To his surprise, he finds not only that the mate is not visible, but that the boat itself is no longer to be seen. At first he thinks that the mooring-ropes have given. Next he imagines that the mate, who is rather a wag, has arrived, and taken the boat further round the bend, for a practical joke. Then he perceives something sticking out of the water. It is part of the mast of the *Griffin*. The ropes have held, but the damage to the boat has evidently been more serious than was at first apparent. She has sunk !

There is nothing to be done but to accept the inevitable. The captain sits down on the bank to light a cigarette and await the arrival of the mate, who, when he sees the state of things, will probably be not over enthusiastic at the prospect of the next few days.

Here is Kehl, the time, and the place, but the mate has not put in an appearance. True, Kehl is

"HE SPORT MAN,
YOU SPORT MAN,"
HE ADDS QUAINTLY.

large, the river-bank long ; but the fact remains that
the meeting-time has come and the mate has not.
Half an hour passes ; an hour, and still the captain
continues his solitary watch. Then he determines to
lose no more time. He seeks out the president of
the "Sport Club" a second time, and after another
interlude of mutual misunderstanding, it is decided
to haul up the *Griffin* bodily, and bring her by road
to Strassburg. A cart and horses are obtained for
the purpose in view. When the unfortunate craft
has been hauled up the stone bank by sheer force—
a party of some three dozen soldiers assisting in the
work—she is borne away to the boat-house.

It is growing dark. The captain is still wan-
dering along the riverside, almost hopeless of ever
meeting the mate, when he sees in the distance
another lonely man, apparently also in search of some
one. The stranger is looking up and down the
river, and is carrying a bag : after every few paces
he peers again into the semi-darkness. There can
be no doubt about his identity. The captain, in a
burst of good-fellowship, shouts to him, waves his
arms, and proceeds towards him, every now and then
stopping to execute a movement which might well be
a figure in some strange war dance. But when he
gets nearer he finds that he is confronted by a perfect
stranger, who is furiously angry at the captain's
childish behaviour and undue familiarity.

"I mistook you for my friend," explains the
captain, in doubtful German. The word "freund"

is the only intelligible one in the sentence. He is more furious than ever. How dare this strange Englishman want to make a friend of him?

The captain, anxious to pacify him, stutters through another sentence, in which the word " boat " brings the light of understanding to the stranger's eye. He thinks the captain is in search of a ferry. He shakes his head and points to the bridge.

" Es sind keine Schiffe da ! " he says.

The dialogue continues for some time, but the captain makes matters worse and worse, until the stranger's wrath has increased so alarmingly, it is to be feared he may develop an apoplectic fit. The Englishman therefore deems it more prudent to disappear as quickly as possible.

After such an encounter he is naturally wary about hailing another person, though presently he catches sight of a man carrying a bundle. He certainly looks like the missing mate. There is nothing to do but to follow until the supposition is proved a correct one. Along the tow-path accordingly the captain steps out ; the distance between the two men grows rapidly less. The nearer he gets, the more sure is the captain that this must be the mate at last. But at the head of the bridge, the man with the bundle suddenly jumps into a tram which is going over the river towards Strassburg. The captain is some forty yards behind. He breaks into a run, but the tram is gone before he has taken twenty steps, and although he follows in the next, he soon loses the track in a regular "Clapham Junction" of electric traffic near the middle of the town. Nevertheless, he spends hours in hunting about in the hope of encountering the mate. Twice he catches sight of the identical bundle in a passing tram, but in each case he is not quite sure enough of its owner to shout to him. The excitement of the chase is so great that he forgets to inquire at the *post restante* for a possible communication until the office is shut. Then he gives up the hunt, and goes to an hotel, and instructs the porter to send to the post-office for letters as soon as it is open, in the hope that the mate may communicate with him.

Oct. 10*th, Strassburg, morning.*—While the captain is still half asleep he is opening a letter which has been brought up to his room. It reads as follows :—

"Hotel Terminus, Strassburg,
"Oct. 9th, 1901.

" DEAR CAPTAIN,
" Where the dickens have you got to ? I missed a train yesterday, and consequently did not get to Kehl until hours after the time arranged. Where is the boat ? I looked everywhere along the tow-path, but saw nothing but a sort of dredger and some swimming-baths. Then I went back to Strassburg. Later in the evening I explored the river banks again at Kehl, but could find no trace of

you or the boat. I thought I saw you once, and yelled out, waving my arms, but it turned out to be somebody else. He was in a furious wax, and said something about giving me in charge. When I explained, or endeavoured to explain, that I was looking for a friend and a boat, he grew 'furiouser and furiouser,' and muttered something about all Englishmen being mad. I don't think I have ever seen a chap so enraged. I thought he would burst.

" I have heaps of other adventures to relate to you when I see you, if ever we *do* meet.

" I have got one clue as to where you are, after all. A man working by the river told me that a 'ship,' with an Englishman, had been taken to the boat-house of the Sport Club. I am therefore going there this morning at 11 a.m. Even if the story is without foundation, we can meet there just the same.

" Yours,

" THE MATE OF THE 'GRIFFIN.' "

At half-past ten the captain is making his way through the outskirts of the town to the boat-house of the Sport Club. When he reaches the canal he perceives, some distance ahead of him, an extraordinary-shaped package. It holds him spell-bound ; his eyes cannot leave it, for it is the very one seen three times last night. For a long time he does not realize that it is moving on in front of him. Then he observes a figure beneath

STRASSBURG
CATHEDRAL.

That Bundle again!

it. It must be the missing man at last. That walk, although its characteristics are somewhat modified by force of circumstance, can be none other than the mate's. That bundle, with numerous articles sticking out of it all round, can only be his friend's. No one else in the world can do up one like that : for, neat in other things as he is, in the matter of hold-alls and kindred parcels his methods are unique. The captain quickens his pace until he is a few yards only behind him. Then the man with the bundle turns round and reveals the features of the long-expected mate of the *Griffin*.

Oct. 13*th, Boat-house of " Sport Club," Strassburg.*—Four days have elapsed since the *Griffin* came out of the water. Not only has she been repaired and overhauled, but various improvements have been made. A wheel has been placed inside the cabin, and this can be connected at will with the tiller. In wet weather it is convenient to be able to steer from below. The sails have been coloured with boiled oil and ochre, and the mate has taken in hand sweeping reforms in the interior arrangements. He is a man of delicate sensibilities—he likes everything done in *recherché* style. Refinement and taste are his weakness. He is particular about his personal appearance, no matter where he is or in whatever circumstances he may be placed. Not that he is in any sense a coxcomb ; but it is a positive pain to him to go without his daily shave or to be

167

compelled to wear muddy boots. He is as methodical as the captain is slovenly. He loves to smoke, reclining amidst luxurious cushions. He remonstrates with the captain for being "so beastly energetic." He wears immaculate collars by day, and dreams in æsthetic-coloured silk pyjamas by night. It has even been asserted (but this is on the captain's evidence alone, and he is a prejudiced witness) that he once had gloves on when he peeled potatoes. Whether this be true or not, it does not alter the fact that the respective habits of the captain and of the mate are as different, in some respects, as it is possible to imagine, even in the ordinary walks of life. But during the last fortnight, the captain, partly through necessity and partly through slackness, has degenerated into a veritable wild man of the woods. The difference between the two men is shown more clearly at this time, inasmuch as the mate has been spending a luxurious holiday in Heidelberg, and, shocked at the household arrangements of the *Griffin*, is bent on innumerable changes. The captain's happy-go-lucky, food-or-no-food, eat-anything reign is over. There is going to be *régime* and *cuisine* hereafter.

A potato-squeezer, an egg-whisk, a colander, several china plates, which are broken at the rate of one in two hours, are added to the kitchen depart-ment. An adjustable shaving-glass, an improved hot-water bottle, a sort of folding reading-stand, (which is quite useless for reading, though it does the folding very well if at inconvenient times) swell the cabin comforts.

It is in vain that the captain remonstrates on the ground that many of these purchases are hardly of a practical nature.

"Just as practical to be comfortable as uncomfortable," urges the mate, cutting at the string of a parcel he has just brought in from a shopping expedition.

"What have you got there?"

"A few more things we shall want," the mate answers calmly. He produces a flat-iron. The captain explodes with righteous indignation, and tells the mate in no measured terms what he thinks of him as a travelling companion on a cruise of this kind. The mate keeps quite calm, and gravely produces a manicure set and a pair of sheets. The captain decides to put his foot down. He insists that this wholesale buying of useless articles shall cease. The mate endeavours to make terms. At last an understanding is arrived at and amicable relations are restored, the mate on his part agreeing not to purchase anything whatever for the *Griffin* without the captain's consent, while the captain on his part solemnly undertakes to countenance several reforms, and to abstain from an alleged habit of drinking beer out of a tea-cup.

Suddenly an inspiration seizes the mate. "A grand idea!" he exclaims, hurling the folding reading-desk into the forward locker in his excitement.

"There's a sort of relation of mine living in Strassburg. We ought to look him up. Let's see, he's the husband of the sister of my brother's wife, or if you like it better," he adds, as he observes that the captain has not quite taken it in, "his wife is my sister-in-law's sister."

THE MATE SMOKES.

"Yes," mutters the captain, feebly.

The mate goes on to explain that his relative is a "merchant," etc., possibly has something to do with river traffic below Strassburg. If this be so, he might be able to get some one to take the *Griffin* in tow. The captain is rather inclined to scorn the idea. After the varied adventures of the boat,

towing seems rather a tame method of navigation.
But he is quite agreeable to pay a friendly call.

"Though I don't see what advice we want,"
he says. "We're getting on all right. Still, I'm
quite game to look up your sister's grandfather, or
whoever it is."

"I think I ought to warn you," continued the
mate, "that these people are probably 'swells,' so if
we *do* call, mind you don't put your foot in it and
give us both away. I know something of German
social customs. There are two things which, above
all others, you ought to bear in mind. Firstly, on
no account sit on the sofa without being invited to
do so. Secondly, if there should be a daughter of
the house, take care never to be left alone in her
company. I know for a fact that if it be only for
five minutes, it will be assumed that you are an
engaged couple. I know what kind of chap you are,
so *do* be careful."

"Hearing you talk, any one would think I was
a baboon," expostulates the captain, mildly.

After a long search and many inquiries of *Polizei*,
who look like military officers, the address is at last
discovered, and the travellers make themselves known
to the merchant and his charming family. They are
welcomed with open arms after the hospitable fashion
of German citizens. On entering the drawing-room,
the captain is about to seat himself on the edge of
the sofa, when he catches an extraordinary expression
on the countenance of the mate. In a moment the

warning flashes across his mind, and there being now hardly one inch between himself and the sofa, he springs to his feet and nervously makes for the most unsofa-like article of furniture he can find.

It turns out that the host is connected with a line of Rhine steamers, and he strongly advises that the *Griffin* be taken in tow by one of these. There is a boat leaving to-morrow morning, and it is the last for several days. If they both agree, he will make all the necessary arrangements by telephone. This plan is discussed during dinner, and it seems so excellent a one that the captain, who at first hesitates, after a few kicks under the table from the mate, thanks his host, and declares himself ready to fall in with the scheme.

IX

IN THE DAVITS

Oct. 14th, on the Rhine near Strassburg (early morn-
ing).—The huge tug, *Badenier IX.*, is snorting
impatiently, and backing both her paddles to hold
herself against the tearing river. The *Griffin* is
being whirled along towards her by the stream, and
her two occupants, each with a scull, control her
movements so that when alongside she drops down,
stern foremost. The mate gets forward and makes
fast a rope thrown from the tug. Then a parley
commences between the captain of the steamer and
the captain of the *Griffin*. Both have to shout their

loudest, for the *Griffin* is almost touching the port paddle-box, and the great wheel churning and pounding the water makes a noise that renders any conversation difficult. And when it is remembered that each is speaking a different language, it is easy to see why no mutual understanding is effected. The mate of the *Griffin*, who, by way of contrast to the captain, is quite a brilliant German scholar, volunteers to interview the master of the *Badenier IX.* at close quarters. Accordingly he clambers on to the tug and goes up to the bridge, where he can be seen apparently delivering a lecture. Within five minutes he returns to the *Griffin*.

The situation is interesting. The skipper of the tug has been expecting to see a steam yacht of some twenty tons, and when a few minutes ago he caught sight of the *Griffin* coming alongside he imagined there had been some mistake. He dare not, he says, take in tow so small a craft. The tug has nothing behind her at present, and therefore will be going at top speed, a pace which would probably sink a boat constructed like the *Griffin*. At first he flatly refuses to take her. Then the mate, after promising to take all responsibility in case of accident, persuades him to consent to her being swung up in the davits.

All this time the *Badenier IX.*, impatient to be off, has been blowing off steam, her powerful engines slowly throbbing and making her vibrate from stem to stern. Now a bell tinkles, and she starts down stream at half speed. The *Griffin* swings round. In obedience to an order from the bridge of the steamer, half a dozen "hands" are summoned, and in a few minutes she is hanging in the port davits. Then the bell tinkles again. This time it is "full speed ahead," and the banks of the Rhine, mile after mile, glide swiftly into the distance.

Events have followed one another with such startling rapidity during the last ten minutes that it takes a little time for the two Englishmen to realize their new surroundings. Here they are, a yacht's crew of two, standing on the deck of a Rhine steamer, while the yacht, which is not a yacht, hangs disconsolately in the davits.

"Looks as though she feels her undignified position," observes the mate. "D'you think those ropes are safe?"

The captain answers the question by stepping across the yawning gulf and causing the hanging boat to swing backwards and forwards. This makes the mate giddy, but it satisfies him, nevertheless.

"A day or two on the Upper Rhine will get you over *that*," says the captain, as the other, gasping for breath, steps across the chasm and clutches convulsively at everything within reach.

They proceed to tidy up things a bit "below deck," and within half an hour everything is in order. Blue smoke fills the cabin, and a contented expression can be observed on the mate's countenance as he reclines amongst cushions, his beloved pipe between his lips. The captain, being a cigarette-smoker, always finishes his smoke first, to the frequent annoyance of the mate, who holds that pipe-smoking is the only true method by which the harmonious equilibrium of things can be maintained. So strongly does he feel on this point, that he frequently gives the captain a curtain lecture on the necessity of pipe-smoking. This lecture is divided into three parts. The first deals with this subject from the medical standpoint. He brings up terrible cases of slow death from cigarette-smoking, but on cross-examination he confesses that the people killed in this way smoked many dozens of cigarettes a day, whereas the captain averages about four. "The principle is the same," he maintains doggedly. The second is from the point of view of economy. He proves that if the captain smokes a pipe he will be able to save a vast sum of money every year. (Where the money is that the mate has saved is not stated.) The third and last is an impassioned appeal to the captain's nautical instincts. For a "land lubber" to discard a pipe for the cigarette is bad enough, but for the captain of a yacht (in these arguments the *Griffin* becomes a yacht) to sink into such degradation, if not actually immoral, at least shows an utter abandonment of seamanlike conduct.

In the Davits of the Badenier IX.—"Let's have *brunch*!'" suddenly exclaims the captain. "It's after half-past eleven."

" Brunch "

" Right you are," answers the mate. " It'll save a wash-up."

A word of explanation is due to all unacquainted with the inner domestic economy of the *Griffin*. The words *brunch* and *tunch* denote meals. When by force of circumstance (as this morning) it is impossible to have breakfast until it is nearly time for lunch, both feasts are rolled into one. This is *brunch*. Sometimes, too, when all hands are required on deck for some hours during the middle of the day, it happens that lunch is driven so late that it is combined with four-o'clock tea. This is *tunch*. Both these meals economize in washing-up, and are frequently resorted to for purposes of time-saving.

When the meal is in progress, the attention of the inhabitants of the *Griffin* is drawn to numerous faces peering at them from the deck of the steamer close at hand. Excited voices and pointed fingers appear to denote some unusual occurrence. What really is the matter is that some of the crew have observed the meal in progress, and are expressing intense, though restrained amusement and interest at the event. That any two human beings can be content in such a confined space is surprising indeed, but that they should revel in this existence, and even undergo it from choice, passes comprehension.

When *brunch* is over, the captain proposes a diplomatic visit to the skipper of the *Badenier IX.*, and the mate, in spite of unpleasant recollections of his last aërial flight, agrees to accompany him. But

the effort has to be made, and this time it seems
easier, inasmuch as there is the expanse of the
steamer's deck to fall on to if needs be. Captain
Wilhelm Paff is found to be a thoroughly "good
sort." Conversation is, of course, limited, but the
mate of the *Griffin* braces himself to the effort, and
really surpasses all previous attempts at German conversation. The history of the Toggenburg craft is

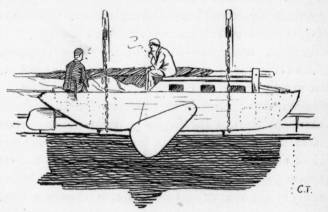

THE "GRIFFIN" IN MID-AIR.

related to the kindly skipper, who nobly tries to show
that he believes it all. The outcome of the conference is that friendly relations are established all
round, and a cabin is placed at the disposal of the
Englishmen. Thither the latter adjourn, having
thanked the skipper cordially, and incidentally having
created an immense impression among the deck hands
of the *Badenier IX.*, but whether this last is caused

by a sporting admiration for the crew of the *Griffin*
or by a vision of possible largess in the near future,
it is impossible to say.

2 *p.m.*—When two men of different tempera-
ments are confined in a space the size of the cabin of
the *Griffin* for a whole day, in which the weather is
wet, cold, and miserable, it is not to be wondered at
that their tempers are shortened. The captain and
mate have had a row. The cause is not far to seek.
Since a cabin on the steamer has been placed at their
disposal, the mate, who has not yet hardened himself
to the new and strange conditions of life on board
the *Griffin*, naturally suggests that it will be more
comfortable for both of them if they take up their
abode on the steamer in the cabin that has been
offered them. The captain, whose hard life during
the last fortnight has made him despise comfort,
selfishly insists on remaining in the boat. Then
the subject is discussed with some heat. The
captain, for his obstinacy in not abandoning the
" ship," is branded as Quixotic ; the mate, for
wanting tolerable comfort, is called effeminate. The
upshot of it all is that the mate, unable to stand the
captain's unreasonable mood any longer, betakes himself to the cabin of the *Badenier IX.*, where, later in
in the day, he receives two plates of steaming soup,
kindly sent as a mark of friendship from the skipper
of the tug. The captain would give anything to get
his share of this, but he is obstinate enough to

pretend not to notice the incident. The fact is that he is feeling the effects of his previous hardships considerably, although he will not confess it, and this cantankerous behaviour is always a sign with him of being thoroughly out of sorts.

Strengthened and refreshed by two plates of delicious soup, and feeling clean and comfortable after a luxurious shave, for which he had obtained unlimited supplies of hot water from the engine-room (much also to the captain's chagrin), the mate proceeds to explore the steamer. He makes friends with several of the hands, and discovers one who can speak a few words of American English. This man is the ship's carpenter, and through being able to converse more freely with the strange Englishman, whom they all take to be at least a duke, becomes thenceforth a man of some importance in the fo'c'sle.

5 p.m.—It has been raining all day, and there is no sign of better weather. The tug is now near Speyer, but the banks of the river are still of the same monotonous type. The mate, pacing the deck alone, feels distinctly cold, and begins to realize that his triumph over the captain is to be rather short-lived; for even the new energy produced by soup and shaving wears off in time. At length his steps lead him to that side of the vessel where the *Griffin* hangs in mid air. What is that subtle aroma which is wafted in his direction ? Surely that is steam which he sees issuing from the well. And then, this strange familiar scent—can it be?—no, not tea? Good old honest English tea?

It is. There is the captain calmly setting out two cups, without saucers, and arranging some lumps of sugar on the board, which serves as a table.

"Tea's ready!" he shouts, opening the hatch, as if nothing has happened, and the mate tumbles into the well and crawls into the warm cabin.

The captain is folding up a large map. "The *Griffin* has just completed her 250th mile since leaving Brunnadern."

X

RHEINLAND

Oct. 15*th.* *In the Davits of the Badenier, IX., morning.*—The mate is the first to wake in the morning. It has been his first night in the *Griffin.*

"Takes some getting used to," he mutters. He stretches one arm out, and then the other. His limbs are somewhat stiff from their contact with hard surroundings. His sleep has been broken; for several times he has started up during the night and gazed down on the surface of the rushing river in utter perplexity at its distance below the boat. On each occasion he has imagined that the tide has gone down and left the *Griffin* high and dry on some precipitous bank. Each time he has roused the sleepy captain and been reminded that the boat is

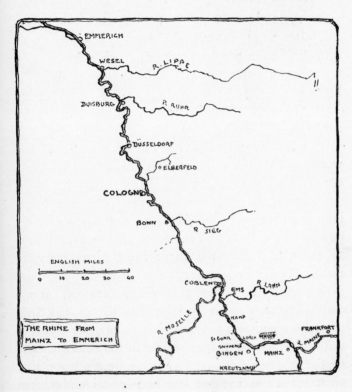

THE RHINE FROM MAINZ TO EMMERICH

hanging in the davits. Now that he can sleep no more, he gets strangely conscientious about early rising.

"Get up! It's six o'clock," he shouts to the captain, who, to his extreme annoyance, is sleeping

as peacefully as if he were in a feather bed. By way
of reply, a strange-looking object like a starfish
under a rug, gives a deep grunt, moves a few arms
and legs spasmodically, and then is still again. The
mate thereupon seizes all the captain's coverings,
and piles them up out of his reach, disclosing him
sprawling upon the floor, with one arm affectionately
encircling a portmanteau. The sleeper awakes and
looks out.

"We've got four barges in tow," he exclaims in
surprise. "When did we pick them up?"

"Mannheim, I think, early this morning. There
was a good deal of shouting and noise, but I couldn't
see what was the matter."

The tug is going round a bend, and the huge
long craft astern are visible from the *Griffin*. Each
one is between two and three hundred feet from bow
to stern, and each has three short masts carrying
booms for working cargo.

In spite of the fact that violent exercise on an
empty stomach is highly injurious, the captain and
mate are compelled to ignore it, or else defer dressing
until after breakfast, for dressing in the confined area
of the cabin of the *Griffin* is not only a science and
an art, it is also a severe test of physical endurance.
The agility of an acrobat and the flexibility of a snake
are the least among the qualities required for the
operation. The captain finishes first, and proceeds
to get breakfast, but the mate, as may be expected,
has not yet developed the right technique, and he

MAINZ.

writhes and struggles and bangs his head against everything for some minutes longer, finally evolving from a nebulous mass of garments, apparently all sleeves, into a dressed being.

"With a little more practice I shall be able to do it as quickly as you can," he gasps. "Then we can exhibit ourselves at the Hippodrome as the champion 'cramped space' dressers of the world. "By Jove," he continues, warming to the idea, "we could make our fortune if we did all this on the stage."

"It would be stopped by the public censor," the captain remarks discouragingly.

"Wait a minute. I have it!" says the mate. He seizes a piece of paper, and, while the captain is making chocolate, draws up the following document:—

THE BROTHERS GRIFFINO,

CHAMPION "TUBE DRESSERS" OF THE WORLD,

will give their celebrated exhibition of skill as
performed before
THE CROWNED HEADS OF EUROPE,
wherein
each will be hermetically sealed for five minutes
in a tube 6 feet high and 18 inches in diameter,
together with a suit of clothes done up in a bundle.
When the tubes are opened
both men
will step out fully dressed in the suits supplied.

Approaching Mainz. — The *Badenier IX.* has slowed down somewhat. There is considerable commotion on board, but the cause is not at first apparent. The captain and mate, from the cabin of the *Griffin,* hear hoarse shouts, but they cannot make out from what direction they come. There is nothing in sight. They both scramble into the well, and then perceive a large boat, almost beneath them, made fast to the steamer. There are two men and a woman on board, and all three are calling attention, by various strange gestures, to the excellence of their cargo of fruit, vegetables, and other supplies which they have for sale. The tug is put at full speed again, and the captive boat, which is built broad in the bow to stand rapid towing, flies foaming and splashing over the water. Meanwhile a spirited bargaining is going on between the crew on the deck of the *Badenier IX.* and the provision-sellers in the craft below. Baskets are held up for inspection, samples are passed up and down, and all sorts of good things are making their way permanently to the deck of the steamer.

"We'd better have some of those," says the captain, as a third lot of rolls is passed up. "You do the talking."

The *Griffin,* hanging in air, is almost exactly over the fruit-sellers.

"Hi!" the mate shouts at the top of his voice, making them look up suddenly in astonishment on seeing a protruding head on each side of the suspended craft.

188

THE LARDER OF
THE "GRIFFIN"
IS REPLENISHED.

A Provision-boat

" Brödchen ! "

" Pang ! " adds the captain, forgetting that French is not understood here by the lower classes.

But, alas ! by the time the astonished vendors grasp the fact that the beings in the mysterious thing above them seriously intend to buy, the last lot of rolls has gone, and there only remains a pile of objects like giant sausages, which on further inspection prove to be loaves of black bread.

" Shall we try one ? " queries the mate.

The captain assents to his share of the risk.

" May as well have some eggs too, and butter," he says, and the mate continues bargaining from the dazzling height of the *Griffin* as though he were giving orders, in an off-hand way, from the deck of a flying machine.

Their attention is then turned to solving the problem both of sending down the money and receiving the goods. The ship's pail is just the thing. It is lowered, containing the necessary coins, and hauled up again overflowing with purchases. In this manner cabbages, cheese, fruit, and other provender find their way into the galley of the *Griffin*.

Half-speed again. The provision-boat pushes off, lets go the tow-rope, and disappears astern to hang on to a train of barges going up stream. These Rhine tugs seldom stop, except at night, and this is their way of getting supplies *en route*.

The Log of the Griffin

Mainz.—At Mainz the *Griffin* is dropped, and the captain and mate, having parted on the best of terms both with the skipper of the tug and with the crew, leave the boat and explore the town. Either it is market-day, or there is a fair in progress, for although the sun cannot long have risen, every street is full, and nearly every open space is packed with stalls, which overflow on to the cobble stones around them. The cathedral, a colossal mass of brickwork looming against the sky, is turning slowly from grey to orange in the warm light of the morning. It dwarfs the market-square, and the busy crowd beneath it looks in comparison like a swarm of gaily coloured ants.

On every side, brought hither by primitive carts, as often drawn by a cow as by a horse, are piles of vegetables, fruit, and other good things from the villages around. The dodges to attract customers are numerous and varied. So determined are the vendors of earthenware goods to call the attention of passers-by, that things are spread all around the stalls in heaps and rows, and it is impossible to pass anywhere near without having to pick a way carefully through avenues of jugs and jars. Before the Englishmen have been two hours in Mainz, they have bought as much as they can possibly carry, and they return to the *Griffin* laden with all manner of things both useful and unnecessary.

Noon.—A clear, bright, breezy morning, quite

192

OLD TOWER,
MAINZ.

hot in the sun. The *Griffin* is now flying down the Rhine at the tail of a train of six huge barges. She is shut in between two colossal rudders, and might be in a lock at low water, but for the fact that the landscape visible astern is continually changing. Village after village disappears into the distance. Bingen is passed, and the vineyards covering the precipitous banks of the river, turned from dull green in places to flaming ochre and old gold by the October sun, are enlivened by little straggling patches of blue and white, where groups of women and children are picking grapes and bearing them in huge baskets to the press.

When the towing-rope is hauled in short, it is possible to climb from the top of the cabin of the *Griffin* into one of the barges. In this way the two Englishmen succeed in getting a more extensive view. It takes considerable time to walk from one end to the other of these enormous hulks, and their decks afford a splendid field for exercise. The men on board are immensely interested in the *Griffin*, and ask her destination. When the mate explains that she has been built in Switzerland, and is on a voyage to England, they seem rather annoyed, evidently imagining that he is making fun of them. In order to restore a feeling of confidence, he thereupon pretends that he has been joking, and that they are in reality making their way from Strassburg to Cologne ; which story, seeming more probable, causes considerable interest.

When the barges are passing Lorch, the sky clouds over rapidly, and when Bacharach is reached, a few big drops begin to fall. The crew of the *Griffin* are driven back to the cabin, and lunch is prepared. At Caub it is pouring hard, and Pfalz, the grim old fortress built in mid stream, can be seen astern only through sheets of rain.

The mate, who has been getting them up by the yard, relates legends of the Rhine during the meal, and has a weird story to tell about every village passed. He is of a romantic turn of mind, and cannot see a ruined castle without finding out if ever in its history a forlorn princess has been immured within. To such lengths does this spirit lead him, that at the moment of one of the captain's greatest triumphs in the culinary art, he crawls out into the rain to get a better view of the Lorelei. Surely the slender chance of scraping an acquaintance with a golden-haired girl with a harp, who lures mariners to their doom, is not to be compared for a moment with the more certain and more solid joy of eating pancakes hot !

Oct. 17*th, Cologne.*—The *Griffin* is now on the end of a train of barges bound for Nymwegen. The weather is still uncertain. Very little wind.

Oct. 18*th, Emmerich, afternoon.*—Emmerich is the frontier town on the boundary between Germany and Holland. Here the Englishmen are taken ashore in

A STREET IN
COLOGNE.

Signing a Document

one of the tug's boats to undergo an examination at the customs house. It is necessary to start rowing towards the bank long before the town is reached, to allow for the strong current. The tug and barges do not pull up until nearly a mile below their landing place, so that in getting back the stream can be allowed for in like manner.

The customs officials have an extraordinary conception of the nature of the *Griffin*, which is alluded to as an " English pleasure yacht." The " captain " is asked to sign a portly document, giving full details as to the crew, cargo, etc. He is also requested to declare if he has on board his " ship " any quantities of dutiable goods. It is soon clear from the obsequious manner of the lower officials that the captain and mate have been mistaken for some important personages from England who are known to be cruising in a steam yacht somewhere near. The joke is too good to throw away. They must live up to the local idea of the English nobleman !

With a tremendous flourish the captain signs the desperate document, declaring that he is not carrying sections of machinery, nor cases of biscuits, nor yet a cargo of sugar. He treats the idea with infinite scorn, and disdains to give trivial details respecting the number of his crew.

By the time the two men swagger out of the customs house the news of their arrival has already got abroad, and a considerable crowd begins to collect. When they see that the Englishmen are wearing Norfolk coats, have their trousers doubly turned up at the bottom, and are, moreover, very untidy, their suspicions are confirmed. These are indeed millionaires ! Into the Kaiserhof they stride, and deign to call for beer. Waiters fly to serve them. The band, which is playing lazily, at a word from the proprietor, strikes up " God save the King." The English lords rise and bow gravely, as though deeply sensible of the honour. Of course, neither of them has anything less than a sovereign

A RHEINLAND VILLAGE.

upon him. The waiter nervously fingers the change. The mate leans forward.

" I suppose, to do the thing properly, we ought to *ignore* change," he says in a low voice. It is the captain's sovereign.

"I think a mark will do this time," the other whispers. " We don't know yet what this adventure is going to cost us."

When they appear in the street again the crowd has grown alarmingly. It will soon be time to

return to the *Griffin*, but, under the circumstances, it will not do to call public attention to the craft. She is lying some way off, it is true, but if the populace began to think for a moment that the insignificant little boat hanging astern of yonder train of barges is the *Griffin*, they will be so enraged at being fooled that the Englishmen will have a rough time of it.

"I forgot getting back," mutters the captain, grimly.

"I'm glad I've squared our bargie not to give us away," the mate whispers. "I told him to wait for us below the town. The other men have gone back, luckily."

There is only one way out of it ; they must walk on and on, until it is dark, and then make a bolt for the boat. Accordingly, the two wretched men start inspecting the town. They point to this and that. They admire this church, that piece of architecture. They treat the crowd at their heels with haughty disdain. On, on, they swagger, covering miles of country, up one street and down another, through this road and along that, while the followers gradually drop away, until they find themselves at dusk in some lonely by-street, but alone !

"Now for it ! " both exclaim together, and they break into a double. Within ten minutes they are rowing hard towards the *Griffin*.

"If we had stayed much longer they would have been off without us," the mate reflects an hour later, as he observes that the tug has weighed anchor.

"I only hope," says the captain, solemnly, "that this incident will not lead to international complications. Anyhow, we have reached Holland in safety."

XI

HOLLANDS DEEP

Oct. 19*th, Nymwegen.*—The tug has pulled up here, and, taking advantage of the stop, the captain and mate are landed in the boat belonging to one of the barges, and indulge in the luxury of breakfast ashore. As they are making their way down to the waterside to return to the *Griffin*, a strange-looking man intercepts their passage. He talks in thick Dutch dialect. The mate, unconsciously feeling the cloak of last night's nobility still about his shoulders, replies in choicest-phrased English. It transpires, after lengthened and excited parley, that the Dutchman wants a tip. Why he should want one, or what he has done to deserve one, or why the Englishmen should be requested to bestow one, is not very clear. All that can be gathered is that the strange man wants a tip, and means to have it. To get rid of him the mate, always generous-minded, offers him a handful of coins, which amounts altogether to slightly over twopence. Instead of being grateful, the man threatens to explode with sheer wrath. He throws the money on the ground, spits on it, stamps his feet, waves large red fists in the air. He hisses unpronounceable names, while the crowd, taking his part, threaten the Englishmen with glaring countenances. The air grows thick with expletives. The captain and mate are beside themselves with perplexity. Eventually it turns out that this strange man is the master of the little tug, which, at the head of a train of barges, has been towing the *Griffin* for some scores of miles, and he does not consider twopence adequate compensation for his work. The truth once established, the captain, full of apologies, tenders four gulden, whereat peace reigns once more, the man beams with satisfaction, the crowd disperses, and the Englishmen return to the *Griffin*.

"There is plenty of wind. Why not sail to day?" asks the captain suddenly, when Nymwegen is growing small in the distance.

The mate rather clings to the easier method of progression, but he cannot find any answer to the question, except that being towed is very delightful, quick, and labour-saving. It is certainly enjoyable to sit about on the boat lazily smoking, while the ever-changing banks fly by. But the *Griffin* is not, maintains the captain, a parcel to be sent from place to place. It is true the weather during the last few days has been generally wet and miserable, in spite of a few bright intervals, and there has been every excuse for slacking. But now the sun has appeared, and it seems likely to stay ; besides, the wind has risen, and it ought to be utilized.

The two men, therefore, board the barge ahead, and explain their new resolve to the hands, with whom they part very cordially.

The *Griffin* is cast off, and, under all her sail, is soon responding to a fresh breeze. Villages, now unmistakably Dutch in character, reveal their position behind the dyke only by their spires or windmills ; for even the bed of the river is higher than their streets.

There is very little in the way of incident to record, until late in the afternoon a large and picturesque town comes into view. The mate, who has made numberless dives into the cabin in order to consult the map, now emerges, and declares that this must be Dordrecht. By mutual consent, the *Griffin* is headed for the wooden quay.

After tying up and making inquiries, it turns out that the surmise is correct, and they are in historic Dordrecht. It is late. The sun is setting in a bath of crimson and gold, and the autumn air is growing chilly. This has been a hard day for the travellers, and, for once, both have a longing for a good civilized bed. "Will funds permit?" is the burning question. A reckoning up is made, with

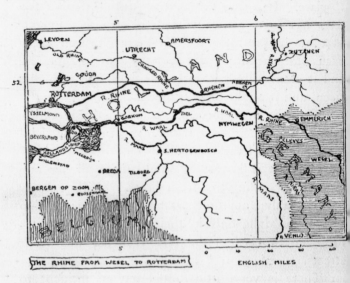

THE RHINE FROM WESEL TO ROTTERDAM   ENGLISH MILES

the result that within half an hour the English-men are reclining comfortably within Les Armes d'Hollande.

Oct. 19th. Nearing Hollands Deep.—High noon, on a grand, clear day! Both captain and mate are in the best of spirits. The *Griffin* is ploughing through the water, and already Dordrecht is dis-appearing behind her. Two or three typical Dutch

NYMWEGEN.

A Rough Passage

sailing-boats with fat sides and huge red sails are on ahead, and the captain at the sheet makes small wagers with the mate at the tiller that the *Griffin* will catch them up. This is not so impossible as at first sight appears, for the smaller craft is able to gain a great deal by cutting off corners.

By this time the wind, which has gradually been increasing since last night, has become a gale, but fortunately, a steady one, and, generally speaking, in the right quarter; so there is every prospect of racing along for some hours. It is exhilarating in the extreme—the boat leaning over with her port bulwarks almost level with the water—the sail well out, and the mast creaking for joy that at last the *Griffin* is exhibiting her full sailing qualities. The captain does not regret that the tackle was over-hauled before starting.

Dordrecht has now disappeared, and the channel is fast widening into an arm of the sea. Huge rolling waves chase one another in endless succession, and now and then break into spray as wind meets tide. It is difficult for the crew to realize the speed they are making, until suddenly a tremendous buoy, the size of a small cottage, passes swiftly across the bows, and disappears in a few seconds behind. It almost seems as though it must have broken loose from its mooring. A man on the look-out from a lighthouse is apparently stricken dumb with amazement at seeing an extraordinary vessel skimming past under his very nose. Perhaps the mate is a little rash in his steering. More than once, to cut off a corner, he takes the *Griffin* across some submerged land where the twigs of bushes brush against the hanging lee-board.

Moerdyke railway bridge is now left behind, and Hollands Deep widens out so that the land on either side is merely a streak on the horizon. A consultation is held, and it is decided to make for Wilhelmstadt, which should be, according to the map, about two hours ahead on the left. The worst of these towns is that they are extremely difficult to locate. Being so far below the level of the sea, it is quite possible to pass a large and flourishing place without being aware of its existence.

For half an hour no word is spoken. Both captain and mate are fascinated by the strangeness and beauty of the surroundings. The vast expanse of water, the crested rollers, caught by the brilliant sunshine, the "plong, plong," as the bow smacks the waves,—all these help to cast a spell over the two voyagers. At about three o'clock a church spire comes into view in the dim distance ahead, and the mate uses it as a landmark for steering. Biscuits are served round to stay the pangs of hunger ; and so the next hour passes.

Wilhelmstadt.—The *Griffin* is now almost in a line with the church, and a look-out is kept for a harbour entrance.

With much difficulty, and after having to tack

THE "GRIFFIN"
IS OBSERVED.

A Dutch Landscape

back, the boat is manœuvred into the small channel leading into the inner harbour. It is a fitting end to the day's adventure. Prolonged exposure to the gale has proved somewhat exhausting; and it is with a sigh of relief that the two men glide gently into smooth water.

The quaintest of sights meets their gaze. In front of them is a delightful little village of brilliantly painted houses, and an old-world pool of placid water with huge posts, apparently hundreds of years old, to which are fastened unwieldy-looking fishing-boats. The transition from the roar of the wind and sea without to the quiet serenity of this little land-locked harbour is almost startling in its suddenness. The captain and mate rub their eyes and pinch themselves to see if they are not dreaming. It seems so unreal for the moment.

There is no excitement amongst the group of phlegmatic Dutchmen on the quay-side as this strange craft enters into their midst. Had it been a genuine Viking boat returning from distant wars, it is doubtful whether their stolidity would have been disturbed. One of their number makes a sign indicating a suitable spot to tie up, and thither the English intruders make their way.

The whole situation is so strange and remarkable that when at length the long-drawn-out tension of the day is relaxed, neither captain nor mate can restrain a hearty burst of laughter. This has the desired effect of bringing home to them the reality of things, and incidentally the demands of hunger. The store is soon doing its duty ; eggs are consumed in alarming quantities, and tea is enjoyed as it rarely is under normal conditions. The climax of luxurious reaction is reached when the cabin is made tidy and comfortable, and the mate settles down to a well-earned pipe, at peace with all the world.

Oct. 2o*th, Wilhelmstadt.*—Contrary to his usual custom, the captain is the first to wake. He leaves the slumbering mate, and takes a constitutional on the ramparts which protect the little town. It is just the morning for a painter. The harbour is sheltered, and its waters reflect in tangled masses the red-roofed houses along the quay, and reproduce white walls and green doorways in wriggling lines of colour. Wilhelmstadt is asleep, and, under a clear sky, lies bathed in sunlight, a picture of peaceful repose, although the noise of the wind overhead, whistling through the skeleton sails of the mill, and the distant boom of breakers show that the tempest still sweeps fiercely over Hollands Deep.

When the captain reaches the summit of the dyke he is nearly carried off his feet by the gale, and after one momentary glance of admiration at the glorious expanse of foam-flecked sea, is driven back to continue his walk by a lower and sheltered path, through a grove of green-stemmed trees. The sunlight, streaming from the east, casts blue shadows across the leaf-strewn ground. At intervals a gap reveals toy-like houses, each with its garden picturesquely stiff; each boasting a tiny drawbridge, which spans a sluggish moat, whereon floating continents of duckweed contrast with the dark depths beneath them.

10 *a.m.*—An event of great importance in the voyage of the *Griffin* has occurred. The mate has been to the post-office, and has received a telegram forwarded from Dordrecht, which summons him to London on business. The captain uses every argument against his going, but in vain, although he makes him promise to rejoin him in a few days. Finally, it is arranged that the captain will take the *Griffin* as far as Veere (this will take two days at least), and there await the mate's return.

The steamer for Rotterdam has left, and there will not be another to-day. Maps, charts, and time-tables are consulted in eager haste, for some railway must be reached by hook or by crook, and at once. The nearest station seems to be Sevenbergen, a town more than ten miles away, and connected by train with Belgium. The captain agrees to accompany the mate to Antwerp. The Englishmen announce their intention of taking this route, much to the consternation of all who hear their plans. The struggles with the language have been long and fierce before the ten-mile journey on foot is decided upon, but there seems no alternative, though heads are shaken vehemently and hands upraised in solemn warning, when the captain points out the intended route on the map.

It is in vain that he is reminded that a steamer crossing Hollands Deep this morning will take them to a little village on the other side. How will it help them to be landed there? The map gives no information on the subject. Nothing further can be elucidated from the stolidly excited Dutch folk. They continue to point to the steamer on the map, while captain and mate, utterly at a loss to know what is wrong with their plans, proceed to pack the mate's delicate wardrobe into a couple of bags, which they sling over their shoulders. As they leave the harbour, they wave a farewell to the group of unsatisfied people, who persist to the last in pointing towards the steamer at the quay.

The weather is glorious, and the Englishmen are undismayed at the prospect of a ten-mile walk. As a matter of fact, they rather revel in the idea. The bags are light, and their spirits lighter. They enjoy the novel sensation of a walk through the flat green country, with its stiff Hobbema-like avenues of tall trees, and its straight roads running along the dykes, above which a distant sail, here and there, is visible, reminding the traveller that he is actually below the level of the sea.

After Wilhelmstadt has been left some three miles behind them, the weight of the bundles begins to tell. The wayfarers shift them from one arm to

A DUTCH BARGE.

A Mirage

another, their feet lag a little, and they begin to scan the length of roadway. Neither makes the remark, yet each secretly hopes for some sort of a lift over the remaining ground. The captain taunts the mate for caving in when the journey has hardly been fairly begun, and declares that nothing will induce him to forego the delights of footing it. The mate replies by asking why the captain listens intently at any sound which seems at all likely to proceed from wheels, and shows such an interest in the road behind. The only answer his companion gives him is a grunt. Meanwhile the bags are bearing the brunt of the argument. They are slung from shoulder to shoulder, across the back, carried on the hip, tucked under the arm. They are even tried on the head ; but whatever the position adopted, their weight seems to be steadily increasing.

A few more miles of this miserable state of things puts an end to any attempt at sociability, and the two men plod along in silence, broken only by an occasional dispute concerning the best road to take, in which differences of opinion it is shown clearly that physical weariness does not improve the temper.

Suddenly, across miles of country, the captain catches sight of a large dome. It looks like some huge marble cathedral, so immense and so shining white that he stops in astonishment. Then he observes that the mate has pulled himself up also, and is gazing at the phenomenon with a puzzled expression on his face. Presently a second dome, apparently a reflection of the other, also stands out in the sky.

"It must be a mirage," says the captain.

"Then you really do see it?" asks the mate, with undisguised relief. "I was just wondering if anything was wrong with me—my eyesight affected by exhaustion, hunger, or something."

"There's nothing marked on the map. It *must* be some atmospheric effect," pronounces the captain, loftily.

"That settles it," says the mate, seating himself on the roadside. "If I don't eat now, there's no knowing what I shall see next. Piccadilly Circus or an A.B.C. would finish me altogether in my present condition of mind."

Such had been the confidence of both men in their walking powers, that they had decided not to take provisions with them, but to wait until they should reach Sevenbergen. Luckily, however, a packet of "grape nuts" has found its way into one of the bags, and this terribly thirst-producing refreshment is produced and eaten, at first with infinite relish, but soon with much difficulty, on account of its exceeding dryness. It is a strange sight, two famished travellers, endeavouring to keep body and soul together by this means, and nearly choking themselves in the effort, for there is nothing whatever of a liquid nature to mitigate their suffering. When the meal is over, the travellers start on again. Cordial

THEY TAKE TURNS IN
PUSHING THE BARROW
AT A VIOLENT RATE.

relations are re-established. Each offers to carry the other's bag, feeling sure that it is heavier than his own. The mysterious domes, however, remain as distinct as before. The only town in their direction is Roosendaal, but they appear much too near for that. The road strikes out in another direction, and they are lost to sight, but to the last there is no explanation as to their nature.

The weight is unbearable by now. After the seventh mile, a halt is necessary every few hundred yards. The conversation resolves itself into a string of condolences. The captain's hands are cut and sore, where the narrow handle has been pressing, and the mate's wrist is suffering from a severe rick.

Another turn in the road, and then a steeple and the waving arms of a windmill herald the journey's end. The two men stagger into the town, and inquire the way to the station. They are greeted with looks of blank astonishment by way of reply. No one seems to understand them in the least. At last the awful truth is revealed. There is no railway here. This is not Sevenbergen. That town is three miles further on !

Tired and footsore beyond expression, the travellers turn away down the never-ending tree-lined roadway, on into the evening shadows. They have given up hoping for the chance of a lift. No carts are going their way. If a sound of wheels behind them cheers them for an instant, depression quickly follows when they realize that it is only the echo of some rumbling carriage approaching them. They struggle on another mile, dragging one leg after the other. Footsore, weary, dirty, famished, with hands skinned and cut, and aching limbs, they are reaching the final stages of mental and physical exhaustion.

But what is that distant rattling noise at their heels?

Down goes the baggage on the ground. The travellers wait breathless, peering behind them, to see what help is coming out of the twilight. The clattering noise grows louder, as two weird-looking figures approach. One of them is wheeling an empty barrow. Into this, as it comes alongside, the Englishmen plump down the bags, without a word of explanation, with a sigh of infinite relief. Far from uttering any protest, the two rustics accept the situation, and delight beams on their faces. They push along with fresh gusto towards Sevenbergen, chattering volubly, and giving all manner of desirable information with regard to distance, trains, and so forth, which the captain and mate, although it sounds like gibberish, feign to understand. It is still two miles to the station, and there is but twenty-five minutes before the train starts. When this fact is realized, the Dutchmen are urged onward, coaxed and encouraged by means of dumb show. The effect of this on the two childish-looking barrow-wheelers, apparently father and son, is to bring to light hitherto unnoticed characteristics. They take turns in pushing the barrow at a violent rate, running on ahead for some fifty feet or so, and then suddenly stopping to wait for the party behind to catch up. This amazing performance is repeated time after time. When the father is taking the lead, the son turns to the Englishmen, and with a meaning look and a gesture towards his forehead, impresses on them that the old man is "wanting." When the son is on ahead, the old man goes through precisely the same pantomime to indicate his son's weak intellect. When the question of the train crops up again, and the mate endeavours to explain that they are going in the direction of Brussels, the strange pair grow wildly excited, and wave their arms in the air. The older man stops dead, puts down the barrow, points towards the south, and in a voice of prophetic warning exclaims—

"Roosendaal, Breda, Bergen op Zoom, Anvers, Mechlin, Bruxelles!" Then he shakes his head violently.

His son strikes a similar attitude, turning towards the north.

"Moerdyk, Dordrecht, Utrecht, Arnheim, Amsterdam, Rotterdam!" he shouts exultingly, nodding his head violently as if the mere mention of these places gives him great joy. They go through all this several times, growing wilder and wilder, gesticulating and screaming out the names of the stations on the railway system with fearful earnestness.

"They mean that one train goes one way, and the other the other," whispers the mate in an oracular voice.

In vain the captain nods his head to the excited men, and protests that no further explanation is necessary. The fact is perfectly clear. He endeavours to calm their feelings by impressing on them that the Brussels train is the one to be caught, at which revelation the rustics are beside themselves with excitement. They point away to the left, across Hollands Deep and shriek out—

"Rotterdam, Amsterdam, Dordrecht, Utrecht, Amsterdam, Rotterdam!"

Then turning round, they turn the other way and mutter "Bruxelles" in a warning voice. They creep up to the Englishmen, who are now standing side by side ready for an attack, and peer into their faces with horrible leers. They shake their fists and draw their fingers several times across their throats. Vain attempts are made to change the conversation, but it inevitably comes back to the same subject. These men are evidently a pair of lunatics, considered harmless and allowed to go about without restraint ; but the word "Bruxelles" seems to have aroused their evil passion. It is very dark, and the long rows of trees on either side make the road still darker.

The captain, in desperation, points to Sevenbergen and exclaims "Beer!" pretending to empty glass after glass, and inviting them to do likewise.

The effect is marvellous. The pair start again towards Sevenbergen. Their weak intellects cannot grasp two ideas at once, and the anticipation of free drinks quite obliterates their rising homicidal tendency.

Still in an uneasy state of mind, the captain and mate notice with no little relief the lights of Sevenbergen, now close at hand. Over the rough cobble stones clatters the barrow into the town, making a noise like a fire-engine and calling forth no end of curiosity and interest. A wild rush is made for the station, but the train has already left, and two hours and a half must pass before another is available. The disappointment, however, is borne with resignation, inasmuch as the interval can be made an opportunity for getting food. Barrow-wheelers and Englishmen repair to a strange little *café* (the only one at hand, for the station is some way from the village), where a meal is ordered by the captain in commanding tones, and the host promises his best fare.

It is a bitter moment for the two famished travellers when it is discovered that coffee and rusks are the most solid form of refreshment obtainable. Nevertheless, a few cups of coffee and several pounds of rusks seem food ambrosial after so long a fast.

Once safe within a well-lighted *café*, the word "Bruxelles" is pronounced without fear. It calls forth renewed threatening gestures from the old man, but an explanation is gleaned eventually to the effect that there are serious riots in that capital, and the murderous looks of the lunatics meant nothing more than earnest appeal to the Englishmen not to go there, especially during this time of the Boer War, either to get their throats cut or to arouse Anglophobia in the mob.

Antwerp, 11.30 *p.m.*—In spite of the lateness of the hour, the travellers, in whom the inner man still cries aloud, insist on knocking up a restaurant and having a solid meal. When they reach their hotel, an hour after this, they are new men. At peace with all the world, and forgetful of the trials and tribulations of the day, they sink into rapturous slumber, in huge feather beds, among downy pillows and caressing sheets.

And while her owners, with characteristic frailty, are surrendered to all the charm of creature comfort, the forsaken *Griffin* is beating out her heart in loneliness, protected only by the dykes of Wilhelmstadt from the hungry, crawling waters of Hollands Deep.

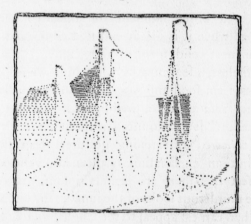

XII

GRIFFIN RAMPANT ON A FIELD SABLE

Oct. 21st, Hollands Deep.—The captain, having re-
turned to Wilhelmstadt by steamer from Meerdijk,
is alone once more in his boat. He has learned
incidentally from an Englishman, who was for some
part of the morning a fellow-traveller, that the
apparently extraordinary behaviour of the people in
trying to prevent the crew of the *Griffin* starting on
their memorable walk to Sevenbergen was capable of
a simple explanation. It appears that the village,
across the water, to which they pointed with such
persistency, is connected with Rotterdam by a little
local railway, and that by crossing thither by steamer

the long-distance tramp could have been saved. No wonder the Englishmen were considered eccentric.

At 1 p.m. the *Griffin*, carrying half a ton more ballast, makes her way, before the gentlest of breezes, out of the quaint little town. The weather is glorious. Great white clouds float lazily in a heaven of deepest blue. Away across the water, the low shores, here and there showing an avenue of pollard trees, are nearly lost in purple haze. The tide is ebbing slowly, and soon a mass of foliage, two small towers, a few dull red roofs, and the arms of a windmill are all that is visible of Wilhelmstadt, which has hidden itself, for the most part, behind its rich green banks. Bathed in mellow sunlight, it casts its image, line for line and colour for colour, in the smooth waters under the shelter of its dykes.

Everything seems to be asleep. Even the light breath, which for a time stirred the surface of the water, has died down, and the *Griffin* floats idly on the tide. Were it not that she passes a buoy at intervals, it would be difficult to trace any movement at all, so faint are the distant shores and so few the landmarks. Far away astern, sails are visible which for some time have been growing more distinct. There must be some wind coming up from that direction. The captain studies them through his glasses. They are barges of the regular Dutch type. Yes, they certainly have got a breeze, and a good one too. There is a white line at their bows.

ON HOLLANDS
DEEP.

Dutch Barges

Flap! flop! The mainsail of the *Griffin* has gybed. In a few seconds she is making two knots an hour. The captain, having his attention fixed on the distant craft, had not noticed the wind on the surface of the water astern. It does not take long for the barges, with their huge spread of canvas, to catch up, for there is little wind low down, and the *Griffin's* mast would run underneath the boom of some of these giants. They are roomy boats with lee-boards, toughly built, and broad in the beam. So silently do they glide by with their sails, russet and yellow, gilded by the evening glow, that the captain can almost persuade himself the *Griffin* has sailed into some mellow old picture, and he feels as though he must be in a dream.

Near Tonge, evening.—The boat is beached, and the captain is trudging inland along a wind-blown route on the top of a dyke, lined with lean and scraggy trees, towards a point where a church tower and the inevitable windmill proclaim the village of Tonge. A group of masts, each with a pennant streaming in the wind (for the evening has brought a change, and it threatens to blow hard before long), tells also that this three-mile walk could have been saved if the *Griffin* had taken advantage of the canal not far distant. After having sent a line to the mate and obtained a few fresh supplies for the morning, the captain makes his way back to the shore, meeting nothing along the dark road but a two-horse sledge

235

laden with faggots. A group of men mark the spot where the boat is lying. They gaze at her as if she were some strange beast thrown up by the tide.

The captain lights the cabin-lamp, and their admiration, blended with amusement at the interior, is considerable. Two of the men appear so interested that the Englishman invites them to come inside and have a look round. They are delighted. The younger and smaller man gets in easily, and the other, a typical Dutchman of colossal proportions, is squeezed through, after some hauling from his companion. The host offers them some beer, which they accept, and a firm friendship is established all round. Everything goes well until the larger man, in making his exit sticks in the hatchway and cannot be moved one way or the other. The captain is beginning to fear for the safety of his precious craft, when his portly visitor is rescued from without, stern foremost.

An exchange of hospitality is inevitable. The Englishman is invited to drink coffee on the barge close at hand. He accompanies his late guests, and climbs down through the hatchway in the forward deck. There is a bright fire burning, and coffee, bread, and cheese are soon upon the table.

The captain knows not a single word of Dutch, therefore a general exchange of ideas is impossible, until, in a moment of happy inspiration, he brings out his chart of the waters of Holland. Here they have something in common. The captain points out place after place, and pronounces each name in a way that is enjoyed by the Dutchmen, who in their turn find towns and villages which have had some especial bearing on their life and history. It is impossible to follow them in many of these comments, but the similarity of Dutch and English in certain words gives a clue to the meaning of some.

A CANAL.

"At this village my mother was born," the captain understands one to say.

He responds by expressing immense pleasure at finding out a fact so interesting and important.

"Here I went to school," the other puts in proudly, and the captain again is overcome with surprise, even going so far as to make a mark in blue pencil near the spot. These are only two examples of the running fire of remarks which continue for some time. Many of them the Englishman is altogether at a loss to fathom, and one, having reference to the big man's missing front tooth, is so obscure that he is unable to grasp its significance, unless it is a reference to the place where he had the misfortune to part with it.

And so the evening wears on. The captain,

A ZEELAND VILLAGE.

assisted by various maps and rough illustrations of a nature realistic rather than artistic, executed in his sketch-book, gives an account of his voyage from the Toggenburg, which causes much jocularity on both sides. In return, the Dutchmen give him valuable information concerning landmarks, beacons, buoys, and sandbanks, and when he leaves he is armed with many hints for his journey in the near future.

Oct. 22nd, North Sea, near East Scheldt, 6.30 p.m.
—A mass of monotonous lead-coloured clouds are tearing across the sky as darkness falls. There will be wild weather to-night. Under a double-reefed mainsail only, the *Griffin* is plodding her way along the Zeeland coast, which can be discerned a few miles distant on her port bow. On the weather side, to starboard, the vast, dreary expanse of the North Sea frets unceasingly under the whip of the gale. Roller after roller at one moment threatens to swamp the boat ; but the next instant it lifts her to its summit, and races on beneath.

The *Griffin* is alone. But for a heavily laden collier which has just passed her, nothing has been within sight for an hour. She has had a rough time since noon, when she began to beat up in the choppy waters of the East Scheldt towards the open sea. Once she has touched a sand-bank, but got off again unhurt, and once she has narrowly escaped going aground on the shore of North Beveland. When she will reach Veere it is impossible to say, for the tide will soon be dead against her, and what its strength will be the captain does not know.

7 p.m.—Although it is quite dark now, and they are needed, it is too rough to keep the side lights burning, for the water is all over the boat, and the well is nearly full. The captain, steering by the compass, is making a course for a point where he imagines the island of Walcheren to lie, but the chart is battened down within the cabin, though it would be little use were it at hand, for there is no lamp alight. By striking a match, which is im-

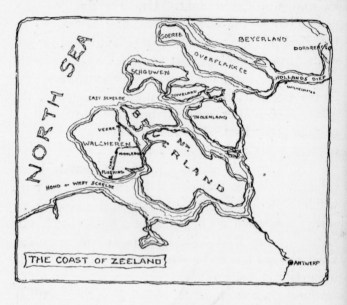

mediately blown out, it is possible to see the face of the compass during a small fraction of a second, but it would be quite hopeless to read a chart, even if the fact be ignored that the captain has only one hand free with which to do everything.

The noise of breakers ahead is unmistakable. What shore can be there, or what sand-bank, the

A ZEELAND WINDMILL.

Breakers

captain cannot tell, but it is enough that it is a
lee shore—and a lee shore on a night like this is to
be given a wide berth. The *Griffin* is running free,
but at the first indication of this new danger the
captain hauls in the sheet and starboards his helm.
In a few minutes he makes out a distant dyke. It
must belong to the island of Walcheren. The roar
of the surf is growing more distinct, so he takes the
Griffin further out, and keeps the shore a mile away.
In the far distance, over the starboard bow, two green
lights are visible. These must mark the entrance to
the canal at Veere. The noise of breaking waves is
alarmingly near. It seems to be on every side.

Suddenly the water gets rougher, and the *Griffin*
begins to run through a mass of foam. She is on a
bank !

Thud ! She is aground ! Then she is lifted up
and carried on, to be stranded once more. Her lee-
boards have stuck for a moment, and she has spun
round with her head to the wind. If she gets broadside on, she will be done for. It is a fearful task to
cling on, but the captain, half-drowned and nearly
shaken to death with the banging of the boat on the
sand, as each wave picks her up and hurls her down
again, manages to crawl forward and cut the bow
stay. Thus the mast comes down with a crash, and
the flapping sail is got rid of. He throws out the
anchor, and pays out more and more rope as the boat
is carried further into the sand. Then he crawls
back astern, and sets the mizzen sail. This steadies

her. There is one hope; the bank does not seem to be a big one, and there is some chance of getting off the other side, if the *Griffin* does not go to pieces first. The captain crawls forward again, and hauls in the anchor. Whenever there is a danger of the boat turning round, he drops it for a moment, and thus holds her head up, and the wind, catching the mizzen, blows the stern round.

VEERE.

In this manner, banged and pounded, the *Griffin*, foot by foot, is slowly manœuvred, stern foremost, across the bank. On both sides, dark patches swept by surf show that she is fortunate in stranding at this point. Had she struck a few hundred feet either way, she would have been doomed; for the tide is ebbing fast.

When the boat reaches deep water at last, on the

other side, the captain throws out the foresail weighted with the anchor and looped in such a way that it forms a drag, which keeps the boat's head to the wind. Then he gets up the mainmast again, but his hands are too benumbed to join the ends of the severed bow-stay very safely, and not daring to trust it with the weight of the mainsail, he hoists a storm jib. Under this and the mizzen, the boat pushes her way through the now more sheltered waters, and within half an hour is running between the two green lights at Veere.

The *Griffin* presents a sorry sight. Half her rigging is hopelessly tangled, and the mainsail and spars are in an inextricable muddle. But the captain is too utterly exhausted to worry about anything. He gives the boat plenty of rope and fixes the anchor in the dyke. Then staggering in his heavy, dripping clothes towards the harbour, he finds the old fortress at its entrance, now known as the Kampveersche Hotel, and introduces himself to the astonished proprietor.

A few hours later, considerably refreshed by food and rest, but still, of course, soaking wet, the Englishman is retracing his steps along the dyke. He would like to sleep ashore, but the desire to get some dry things for the morning makes him decide to return to the boat. It is too dark to see anything but a pale line of phosphorescent fire, where the waves are beating themselves against the sea wall. The wind is still as boisterous as ever, and it is difficult to keep a footing.

For a long time the captain gropes about, unable to find the spot where he left the *Griffin*, but at last he stumbles upon the anchor stuck in the dyke. Considering that there was plenty of slack rope when he left, he is not a little surprised to find it now quite taut, and he hopes, fervently hopes, that the tide has not been playing tricks with the boat and hung her up on the dyke. He follows the rope down the

DRENCHED.

slope to the water's edge, and his hopes dwindle into fears. Then the incident at Kehl flashes across his mind, and, taught by that bitter experience, he peers into the darkness to see if he can make out, not the *hull* of the boat, but a few feet of the top of the *mast*. At first he tries to persuade himself that what he sees is a pile or beacon to mark the channel, but posts in the water do not usually have sprits.

Shipwrecked

There is no getting away from the fact: the *Griffin* has sunk. She has been hung up on the dyke when the tide went down, and has been filled as it rose again.

There is only one thing for the shipwrecked one to do, and that is to return to the hotel. He does so, to the astonishment of the host, who had indeed thought him mad when he had started out a little before midnight, refusing a bed, but who thinks him more insane still now that he returns in the night, knocks him up, and insists on having one.

But the captain is far too tired to go into any explanation, and he is soon asleep. Meanwhile, his clothes are steaming furiously before a stove, especially stoked up for the occasion, in an energetic and praiseworthy attempt to get themselves dry before the morning.

C.T.

XIII

THE ISLE OF CALYPSO

Oct. 23rd, Veere.—The morning breaks crisp, clear, and exhilarating. The wind, though still boisterous, has shifted a point or two northward, and the white crawling surf seems less terrible now that it lies spread out in sunlight. The slender grey belfry spire of the Stadhuis rises over roofs, white walls, and quaint gardens, side by side with the squat tower of the huge brick church, in playful and fantastic defiance of the laws of proportion. The green banks along the sea wall, planted with rows of slender trees, the shining, golden masts with flying

248

pennants, picked out by the sun against the green-blue sky, the diminutive courtyards neatly bricked and decorated with quaint devices in tiles, the toy-shop realism of women who carry pails of milk or loads of butter, all speak of a peaceful and unbroken routine of life, compared with which yesterday seems a veritable nightmare.   Surely it was one, and this is the awakening !

Breakfast is served in the old tower which stands at the entrance to the harbour, and from the window at the table-side it is possible to see all that is passing on the wooden landing-stage below.   Two small sailing craft have just put out, and are making their way across to North Beveland.   A group of little girls, with white head-dresses and bare arms, looks like a gathering of dainty Dutch dolls.   They are throwing breadcrumbs to the gulls.   The captain is in the act of raising a cup of coffee to his lips, when his eyes are fixed immovably on a girlish figure which has appeared suddenly on the scene.   It is impossible to drink and look sideways out of the window at the same time, so the cup has to be put down again.

To say that the new-comer is pretty is a tame way of indicating her charms.   As she stands there in the sun, with a little basket tucked under one of her plump bare arms, laughingly throwing pieces of bread into the air for the sea-birds to catch, she is a picture of everything enchanting that can be found in a maiden of eighteen summers.   That bare head, with its wavy hair like polished ebony, divided in the middle into two rich masses; that fresh round face, out of which peep roguish black eyes; that flash of white which shows through parted lips when she tosses back her head to laugh at the antics of the circling birds; those lips that seem——

But all this is out of place in a ship's log, which deals only with sober records of events connected with navigation.

The door opens, and a portly gentleman enters the room. He greets the captain with some exclamation, probably the Dutch for "Good morning!" In returning the compliment, the Englishman is compelled to turn his eyes momentarily from the vision through the window. When he can get a chance to look out again, the children and the gulls are alone visible; the girl has gone.

The captain, when he has finished his now cold coffee, endeavours to enter into conversation with the aristocratic-looking personage who has just arrived, but it is impossible to get very far. The excitement of a game of billiards, however, is something which both men can understand, and several are played, in which Holland is invariably victorious. Within two hours the chance acquaintances have become quite friendly, and the Dutchman insists on a return match at his house. The captain manages to understand the invitation, but fails utterly in explaining why he is compelled to decline it. Of course, the *Griffin* must be raised, and the morning

THE STADHUIS,
VEERE.

is now far advanced. It is in vain that he brings out his sketch-book, and endeavours to elucidate matters by means of drawing and gesticulation. The old gentleman cannot make head or tail of his story. Then, as if some idea has struck him, he walks over to the window, throws up the lower sash, and leans out.

"Lutwine!" he calls to some one unseen below.

A musical voice answers; there is a light step in the passage, and a girl comes tripping gaily into the room.

When she sees a stranger she stops suddenly. The captain recognizes the charmer whose attractions had so interfered with his breakfast, and blushes to the roots of his hair. He bows awkwardly, and the Dutchman whispers something to her in Dutch, She looks up at the captain, and then says demurely—

"My father wish that I speak the English of you."

The captain again tells his story, interrupted at intervals by exclamations in pretty broken English on the part of the fair interpreter, and it is translated, sentence by sentence, to the amused and interested Dutchman. This gentleman turns out to be a resident of importance, holding a position equivalent to that of mayor or burgomaster. He expresses the greatest sympathy with the shipwrecked Englishman, and asks him to come to his house to "coffee" at four o'clock. Needless to say, the captain accepts the invitation with the greatest pleasure, although he devoutly wishes a clean collar and a few other articles of dress had been saved when the boat went down.

Why this sudden love of order on the part of the master of the *Griffin*? Has he not frequently laughed to scorn the very same trait in the mate's character? Are not the clothes of an "English lord" in Emmerich good enough for Veere?

Afternoon.—A great deal has been accomplished within the last few hours. The *Griffin*, which was unloaded at low tide, has been floated again and towed round to the harbour. The crews of the various "schlutes," lying at the quay, have between them taken in hand the drying of the soaked rugs and clothing, and the mate has been informed by letter of the whereabouts of the *Griffin*, although the captain has not the courage, remembering, as he does, the Strassburg incident, to tell him of her condition. He will probably be here in two days or less.

It is four o'clock, and the captain, punctual to the minute, is nervously knocking at the door of the burgomaster's house. He has made a pathetic attempt to smarten himself by brushing his clothes thoroughly and changing the colour of his sodden boots from grey-brown to a dull black. These alterations, together with such advantage in tone as can be given by the turning of his collar, are the result of an hour's patient effort.

GROOTE KERK,
VEERE.

An Afternoon Call

The door is opened at last, and the captain is shown into the presence of the burgomaster and his charming daughter. The latter, whose English has been learnt at school in Switzerland, again volunteers her services as interpreter, so that the captain and his host are able to exchange remarks. There are charming mistakes and amusing misunderstandings, but the time flies all too quickly to the Englishman, who thoroughly enjoys this novel method of conversation. The upshot of it all is that the burgomaster's house is placed at his disposal. He is invited to come when and as often as he will. He is pressed to bring his drawings. Every assistance is promised by the hard-worked interpreter.

The prospects of the next few days are considerably brightened, the captain's one regret being that he has so selfishly hastened the mate's return to the scene of action.

Oct. 24th, Veere, morning.—Is there to be a regatta at Veere to-day? Why are the shrouds of the schlutes decked with such strange-shaped and many-coloured flags? The captain strolls down to the quay to get a nearer view. He beholds upon the rigging of the various boats in the harbour, blankets, rugs, handkerchiefs, coats, trousers, stockings, and a hundred and one other articles of salvage stock from the *Griffin*, blowing in the morning breeze. It is a somewhat public exhibition of the captain's wardrobe, but the wind and the sun together will not be long in doing their work. No amount of airing, however, will make sodden collars wearable.

The captain, on this account, makes a journey into Middelburg, four miles distant, and obtains supplies of clean linen, which greatly increase his self-respect, so that when he pays his second call at the house of the burgomaster, he feels considerably happier.

Oct. 25th, Veere, evening.—The mate has at last arrived. The *Griffin's* second submersion is recounted.

"You always give me a wet and cold reception of this kind," he says jokingly. The rendezvous on the river bank at Kehl had not been forgotten.

The captain has been spending the greater part of the day at the house of his new friends, and has promised to take his companion round to see them later in the evening. The mate agrees to accompany him after dinner at the hotel—a very special dinner, in honour of his arrival.

The cuisine for the most part is excellent, the wine good, but there is one grotesque incident. It is, of course, considered by these simple people impossible for Englishmen to have a really good meal without beef-steak. Accordingly the dish *de resistance*, produced with much unction, and evidently intended to make the visitors feel thoroughly at home, consists of two enormous slabs of this savoury meat. But, alas! it is impossible to get the knife through them, although both men wrestle with the indiarubber-like masses, taking it in turns, so that each might relieve his exhausted companion.

"It is no use," sighs the mate, as he puts down the knife and fork resignedly. "We must give it up."

"But they will be mortally offended if we send it back untouched," urges the captain. "It is the dish of the evening. We must make some pretence of eating it."

The mate glances out of the window at the sea, which is washing the base of the old fortress.

"The tide is up," he says significantly.

The captain springs to his feet and listens at the passage. All is silent. Then with a wild light in his eyes, he puts his back against the door.

"It must be done," he hisses between clenched teeth, "and that quickly."

Within a few seconds the window is thrown open, and the beef-steak, slab by slab, is hurled into the sea.

A step can be heard in the passage.

"Just in time. Shut the window and sit down," the captain whispers excitedly.

There is a moment in which to smear gravy over the plates and to give the knives and forks an appearance of recent use. Then the servant enters with a dish of steaming vegetables. She is struck dumb. These Englishmen, true to the traditions of their country, have not only demolished the beef-steak in an incredibly short space of time, but they are positively waiting for more, and looking as if nothing at all unusual has happened.

After this exciting meal is over, the captain, according to his promise, takes the mate round to the burgomaster's house. The drawings, which he

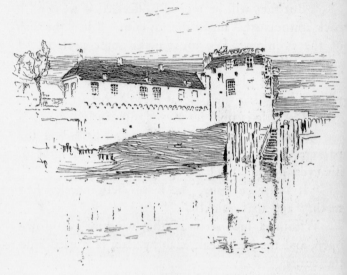

THE OLD FORTRESS, VEERE.

has made the *raison d'être* of many former visits, are all exhausted, and to-night he goes empty-handed, though not on that account doubting his welcome. The mate, however, who has no sketches to show or adventures to tell—the captain has told them all— feels that he will not shine in Dutch society. He begs the captain to let the visit be as brief as possible.

"We ought to get under way to-morrow," he remarks.

The captain shrugs his shoulders doubtfully.

"The boat is still damp," he objects.

"Rot!" retorts the mate. "We can't stay fooling about here and spending our time in going to Dutch 'at homes.' Besides, the boat is no

A MILK-CART.

damper than it was at Strassburg, and you didn't mind *then!*"

The burgomaster's daughter greets both visitors with great cordiality, and after introducing them all round, chatters away in broken English, much to the disgust of several young military men present, who resent the disturbing element in their slow-going midst. The mate comes out of his shell, and is a great success, utterly eclipsing the captain. He makes the most elegant bows to the ladies. He goes so far as to kiss the hand of the burgomaster's wife! When the daughter plays, he turns over the music for her. When she sings, he accompanies her. He even obliges with a song in his rich tenor, which fairly " brings down the house." He joins in duet after duet with the fair soprano. Altogether, he is a colossal success. Early in the evening he is nudged by the captain.

" Time to go, old man."

" It's early yet," replies the mate, casually.

" Thought you wanted to turn in early," urges the captain, maliciously.

" Nothing of the sort," replies the mate, hunting for more songs.

The evening wears on, but no persuasion will prevail with him, and all the other guests have departed before the captain succeeds in dragging him away.

" You forget you want to start away early to-morrow," snaps the captain.

" Well, there's not such a desperate hurry. The boat, as you say, is still damp. We can decide the question in the morning."

Oct. 26*th*, *Veere*.—Midday still finds the *Griffin* moored to the quay in the harbour of Veere. A thorough examination has been made of the boat, and both captain and mate agree that it will not do to run the risk of developing rheumatic fever during

MIDDELBURG.

the last week of the cruise. The boat is still a little damp. It is best to be on the safe side.

The afternoon is spent at the house of the burgomaster, where the piano helps towards the mate's continued popularity. The captain's nose is much out of joint. He cannot talk to any one, because his interpreter is practically glued to the music-stool. In despair, he attempts a little badinage with the burgomaster's second daughter, a young miss of fourteen, the owner of two stiff plaits of flaxen hair. The mate discovers them *tête-à-tête* in the hall, and shows violent disapproval.

"I say, man, you *must* be more careful. Don't you know you'll be expected to marry the girl, if you compromise her like that?" he protests, in an agitated voice, when they are alone.

"Compromise? I was merely showing her how English girls play hockey."

"All the same, you'll have to propose for her if you call again. It's the custom of the country. It's a good thing we are leaving in the morning. I would not dare to go to the house again."

Oct. 27th, Veere.—The mate has refused to put to sea in what he describes as half a gale. It would be ridiculous, he maintains, to come from Switzerland to Holland in safety, and then to be wrecked nearly at the journey's end. The captain is compelled to submit, and before the morning is very far advanced the two men find themselves at the burgomaster's.

In the evening they call again, this time to say farewell. As before, the master of the *Griffin* finds the time hang heavily, while the mate and the lovely Lutwine make music ; and he longs for the morrow, when, gale or no gale, he is determined to get under way. Whatever the weather, it will be possible to reach Flushing by canal, through Middelburg.

The burgomaster has gone to sleep in his large armchair, and the mate, having exhausted all the music in the house, has begun to expound the science of palmistry to his fair accompanist. The captain, the only other person in the room, is having a slow time. He boils with righteous indignation, for he knows perfectly well that his rival is entirely ignorant of the subject, and is using it only as a pretext for holding the girl's hand for nearly three quarters of an hour.

Later in the evening, nevertheless, he takes sweet revenge. The host, after a short nap, has roused himself again, and the captain persuades him to give them a song, and arranges with masterly cunning that the mate shall accompany it. It is a ballad of some twenty verses, very long ones too, and it is evidently of a humorous nature, although not a word is intelligible to the Englishmen. This is the captain's chance. He asks the blushing Lutwine if she understands phrenology. She does not. He goes on to explain (at the other end of the room) that it is far more trustworthy a science than palmistry, and illustrates it in a practical manner. The

THE MATE
SCORES.

Farewell !

worthy burgomaster, singing away at the top of his voice, has fixed his attention on the words of the song ; but the mate, who by the third verse has got the accompaniment off by heart, can see, in a mirror over the piano, the phrenological studies in progress. There are still thirteen more verses, and he is nearly mad with jealousy. He finds himself playing *fortissimo* passages with the lightest of touches, lest the piano shall drown fragments of "scientific" conversation at the other end of the room ; while those marked double *pianissimo* sometimes coincide with a touching tableau in the glass, which causes him to thump the instrument in impotent rage.

When the item is over, the two visitors congratulate the singer. The girl explains that it is a comic song, whereat the captain replies that it is one of the funniest things he has heard for a long time.

When they take their leave, late in the evening, they say farewell for good. The *Griffin* sails at sunrise. The burgomaster and his family wish them good luck on their voyage, and invite them most cordially to come and see them again if ever they should find themselves in the Island of Walcheren.

The captain feels that he has distinctly scored this evening. As they return to their hotel, the mate is heard to mutter in melodramatic fashion under his breath—

"Ha, ha ! a time will come."

269

The Log of the Griffin.

Oct. 28*th*, *Veere*.—By seven o'clock all is ready to put out to sea. The mate is still reluctant to depart, and seems to be expecting the wind from a new quarter. Presently his actions grow brisk.

"The trysing line is caught. Just see to it, will you, while I cast her off?" he observes, as he scrambles ashore to loosen the mooring ropes.

FLUSHING.

Meanwhile the captain, buried in the half-furled sail, is clinging on to the mast with one hand, and disentangling the cord with the other. He cannot see the mate, but he can hear him in conversation with some one. There is a girlish voice answering him.

Before he has unravelled the sail the boat has been pushed off, and the mate has sprung on board again. The captain clutches hold of the bow stay, ducks his head under the jib, and just catches sight of the burgomaster's daughter waving a farewell from the quay. Then the old wooden landing-stage cuts off the view, and the *Griffin* begins to respond to a freshening breeze.

The mate is smiling. He laughs best who laughs last.

Oct. 28th, Flushing, evening.—The *Griffin* is lying under the shelter of one of the mail boats. A great event has happened. The mate has made the acquaintance of the captain of one of these steamers, and the two adventurers, boat and all, have been offered a lift in the davits.

"Most unromantic method of travelling," murmurs the captain.

"Don't be a fool," replies the mate. "You know, as well as I do, that with weather like this we shall be a week getting to England, and to do that we shall have to hug the coast under the shelter of the banks, down to Dunkirk. Now, if we accept this offer, we shall be off the Kentish coast to-morrow morning."

"Why are you in such a desperate hurry?" the captain asks, "You have not minded wasting the last few days."

The matter is finally settled in favour of the quicker method.

When night falls, the *Griffin*, her ballast for the

271

most part having been emptied into the sea, is hauled into the davits. One of the blocks jambs, and a direct pull is necessary to get her stern high enough. All the steamer's hands are summoned on deck. Black and half-naked men appear from depths below, and loafers on the quays lend their aid, until some forty or fifty men, a motley crowd indeed, lighted by lurid and flickering torches, succeed in getting the boat in position.

Before midnight, Flushing is growing indistinct in the distance, and two figures can be seen on the Queenborough boat, peering astern, each unobserved by the other, in vain attempt to catch a glimpse of some roof or spire on the receding Island of Walcheren, which may mark the whereabouts of that most delightful of places, the village of Veere.

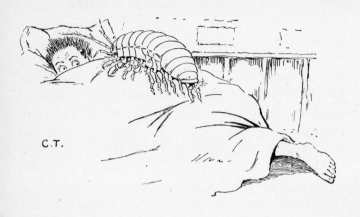

C.T.

XIV

THE CLOVEN HOOF

Oct. 29th.—At dawn the Kentish coast is just visible.
A fresh breeze is blowing, and the cold green surface
of the sea is broken here and there by white patches
of foam. A dozen or more barges, heavily laden,
are ploughing their way steadily before the wind,
out of the Medway and heading up the river towards
Gravesend. The Nore is soon left astern, and
Sheerness lies a mile on the port bow. Everything
is made ready for lowering the *Griffin* into the sea
again, and when the somewhat surprised customs
men have ascertained that she is nothing contraband,

273

she is let go at Port Victoria. There is no ballast on board except a few hundredweight of pig-iron, so the captain and mate, not daring to set sail, paddle her, wobbling and unsteady, towards the sandy shore, near the village of Grain, and there let the receding tide leave her high and dry on the beach.

When the sun is up, all the clothes and rugs, still decidedly sticky and damp after their immersion at Veere, are spread out on the beach to dry. This task takes nearly an hour, for the breeze is strong enough to blow up the edges and corners of everything in a way that necessitates the addition of a vast number of stones to weight them down. The effect when complete is most imposing : blankets of many colours, and garments of every description cover the ground for a considerable area around.

3.30 *p.m.*—There is now hardly an hour and a half left before the *Griffin* will be afloat, and not only has she to be ballasted, but all the things on the beach have to be got on board again.

In this work the two men are assisted by a coast-guard, who, attracted partly by the blaze of colour caused by the blankets, and partly by professional doubts as to whether such an odd-looking thing as the *Griffin* may not be some new smuggling dodge, has good-naturedly offered to help in the race against the tide. The sacks are filled with sand and stowed away. A difficulty presents itself, nevertheless. The beach is swarming with sand-fleas, and it is quite impossible to fill the sacks without including some dozens of these creatures, ranging from the size of a horse-fly to that of a shrimp. It is to be hoped that they will not be able to get through the sacking, or there will be a lively scene on board to-night.

Evening.—The *Griffin* is at anchor now between Queenborough and Sheerness, and supper is ready. This has been prepared by the mate with numerous mysterious dishes of his own invention. This is the *Griffin's* first night in English water, and, now that she has come so far unhurt, it is natural to expect that the crew will be in good spirits. But, somehow, in spite of obviously forced jocularity, there hangs a gloom over both adventurers that is very noticeable. Each looks as if he has a great and secret fear gnawing at his heart.

A small sand-flea suddenly appears in the salt. It is at once dispatched by the mate.

" Must have got in with the rugs," he says.

" Yes," responds the captain, gloomily, " it must."

Then the meal proceeds again in silence. A few minutes later there is a clicking sound, and another creature drops suddenly into the captain's tea.

"Are you sure you shook all those blankets ?" the mate asks, as he reaches over and pulls out the thing with the handle of his fork.

" Quite," replies the captain.

Another silence.   Then the mate drops his voice to an agitated whisper pregnant with meaning.

" I suppose they can't get out ? "

" Get out of what ? "

" The sacks."

" Impossible ! "   The captain is quite touchy about it.   " Do you suppose things like that can get through sacking ? "

" Of course not ; but I was thinking that possibly —in fact, I remember now—— "

" What ? "

" That some of the sacks had holes in them ! "

The captain groans, and what the mate says does not concern this narrative.   It is no use hiding the terrible truth any longer.   In a few hours the cabin will be alive !   In vain a hunt of extermination is organized.   In vain rugs are spread skilfully over the ballast to prevent further reinforcements joining the enemy.   In vain do the wretched occupants of the boat wrap themselves thickly in bedclothes.   Leaping from the floor, crawling up the sides, and then dropping from the roof, a continual and ever-increasing cannonade of creatures like anæmic shrimps, makes night loathsome, and sleep, but for a snatch now and then, impossible.

Oct. 30*th.*—When it begins to get light the captain perceives, on the edge of a blanket, what appears at first to be a full-sized lobster crawling stealthily towards him.   He wakes the mate with a

The Effect of Perspective

shout of terror, but it proves on further investigation that this fearful apparition is the effect of perspective on a sand-flea a few inches from the observer's eye, causing it to appear about a quarter the diameter of the cabin. Both men look ten years older since last night.

Without a word being spoken, they realize that breakfast is impossible as yet, and that the only thing to be done is to get off as quickly as wind and tide will allow. The anchor is up in a minute, and the mainsail trysing lines let go. There is no need of mizzen or foresail, for the *Griffin*, heeling over to a beam wind, is soon making her top speed through sheets of rain, now and then lying down suddenly to a gust at such an angle that she threatens never to get up again, her blunt bow noisily smacking the water and churning it into a frothy track astern. And so past Queenborough, up the Swale, under the bridge that leads to Sittingbourne, two haggard men may be seen this morning, flying as though from a pestilence, to seek a secluded haven where they can turn out their belongings and free the boat from her too lively ballast.

The mate is forward of the mast on the look-out. The captain at the wheel is unable to see anything over the port bow on account of the sail.

" What's ahead ? " he asks.

" A small village and a cement factory."

" The very place for ballast. Keep your eye open for a landing-place," shouts the captain. " We must bring up here."

The Log of the Griffin

"Starboard a bit!" sings out the mate, excitedly. He has evidently seen something. "Let go the sheet, and put her hard over."

In a moment the sail is trysed up by the mate, and the captain can see that the *Griffin* is making her way up a very narrow and winding channel, out of which run numerous arms. These lose themselves in tortuous mazes among tracts of short grass and weeds. The wind on the furled sail, together with the way on the boat, is sufficient to take her along slowly until she is moored to the bank at the end of a narrow channel, the field on each side almost touching her. The place seems to have been specially designed by nature as a ground for camping out. From a distance of a few yards, the *Griffin* seems to be unaccountably stranded in a plain of grass some hundreds of feet from the river.

"Breakfast ashore?" suggests the captain.

"Rather!" responds the mate. Before many minutes have passed, although it is still raining, the kettle is merrily boiling, and a rough tent has been improvised out of sails and spars.

Evening.—The *Griffin* is thoroughly cleared out, the sacks carried to a safe distance and emptied, and the sand-fleas exterminated. It remains to explore the village, not half a mile distant, and to call at the cement works in quest of ballast.

"It's not a very lively place, this," says the mate, as they near a small row of cottages. "I haven't seen a soul to-day, have you?"

ON THE SWALE.

" Not one."

They draw nearer. It is now getting dark, and it seems strange that there is not a light of any kind.

"What's the matter with the windows?" the captain asks.

" And the doors?" chimes in the mate.

THAMES BARGES IN A MIST.

Both stop short. Every window and every door is boarded over or covered with corrugated iron.

" Must be to let," mutters the captain. "How much bread did you say we'd got?"

" About four cubic inches," says the mate, precisely.

They walk on to the next group of houses.

" Very quiet," observes the mate.

"Very," the captain assents. "Perhaps every one is at the Works."

"Then they must be jolly well afraid of burglars," retorts the mate, as he gazes blankly at another set of nailed-up doors and windows. "Let's go back."

"We must leave here in the morning," exclaims the captain, "or we shall starve. What about the ballast?"

"THE OLD HOUSE AT HOME," QUEENBOROUGH.

The mate does not answer the question for a moment. Then he points towards the Works. They, too, are evidently deserted.

"Why not explore a bit, anyhow?" he asks.

"Why not?" wearily answers the captain.

He is thinking of that four cubic inches of bread.

It is now getting dark. Torn clusters of black cloud sprawl across the sky and hurry overhead.

TWO FIERY EYES
PEER FROM THE
DARKNESS AHEAD.

Uncanny

The wind is uncertain and boisterous, sometimes dropping to a calm for a moment, and then, with a shriek, seizing a bush or a tree, shakes it furiously. The two explorers climb through a ragged opening in the wall of the cement factory, and find themselves in a paved court, out of which open black vaults and winding passages. Against the sky loom chimneys of every size and shape, and grated windows looking down into unknown depths bring to mind stories of goblins and gnomes and wicked wizards. Through room after room, passage after passage they wander. In one, a rusted wheel discloses traces of what was once machinery. In another, the walls, tottering with age or infirmity, are bound together with bands or girt with chains. Through all the wind moans dismally.

" What a weird place ! " whispers the mate.

" And not particularly safe. If the wind gets up a bit more, we may have a brick or two dropping on our heads."

They enter a long passage, quite dark, and grope their way along the wall.

" What's that ? "

They both stop instinctively, for at the same moment they become conscious that they are in the presence of some third being. There is a swishing noise and two or three faint taps.

" Is anybody there ? " asks the mate in a polite tone.

For answer, there is a snort or a laugh of defiance. It is not loud, but there is something uncanny and diabolical about it. The captain has a box of lucifers. He takes about six in his hand and strikes them all together, but the wind blows them out immediately. But what he sees in that flash is enough. Two fiery eyes peer from the darkness ahead.

"Great Scott, do you see that?" he gasps, and a black shape glides up to them. They crouch down against the wall, and as it passes they can feel a hot breath on their faces. The captain is prepared to swear that he smells sulphur.

"The devil is in this," he says, as they return to the *Griffin*. "I would take my oath I saw a cloven hoof!"

"I saw four!" said the mate, solemnly.

"And what about the sulphurous smell. There was no doubt about that," argues the captain.

"Don't buy cheap matches," is the short reply, and the subject is dropped.

XV

THAMES TIDES

Oct. 31st, Swale, Thames.—Before the sun has been up half an hour, the *Griffin* is alongside the quay of the deserted cement works, and a cargo of miscellaneous kind has been taken aboard for ballast. The wind is fresh, but rather unsteady. Supplies for two days are taken in at Queenborough.

It is not until Gravesend is reached that the Swiss-built craft attracts much notice. But when she has to run the gauntlet of the tugs and pilot-boats lying along the shore below the town, she creates great amusement, and as the tide is against

her, she is compelled to drop anchor in their midst.
Then a running fire of merciless chaff commences,
and is maintained until darkness falls.

"Look out, Bill, 'eres a torpedo a comin' !" is
the opening shot. One man expresses a conviction
that the *Griffin* must be the *Flying Dutchman*, while
another shouts out a mock order to man the yards.
It is often difficult to think of a suitable reply on
the spur of the moment. Generally fragments of
Flemish, in the way of repartee, seem to command
the greatest respect.

"It requires more courage," remarks the captain,
"to bring the *Griffin* up the Thames than is necessary to take her all the way from Switzerland to
England."

Nov. 1st, Thames.—At dawn the *Griffin* is under
way, and is taking advantage of the flowing tide.
Tilbury and Gravesend are soon indicated only by a
few lights, growing paler as the morning breaks.
Three or four topsail barges and a "stumpy" are
working their way up the river, and ahead of them
a black and ghostly looking collier, deeply laden, is
pouring forth columns of smoke, to hang in gloomy
clouds over her track astern.

The sun is up before Greenhithe is reached, and
soon a continual stream of traffic is passing London-
wards. Craft of all kinds and sizes, under steam,
under sail, tramps, liners, tugs, timber-ships from
the North, orange-boats from the South, grain-boats,

cattle-boats, all are coming up astern and passing on ahead, a motley crowd indeed !

Among these "Thames types," great and small, the *Griffin* works her way, causing much merriment, and bringing to light many a joke hoary with age.

DAWN.

The tide turns against her when she reaches the poetic district known as Bugsby Marsh, and not far from the two huge gasometers thereon she drops anchor, to wait for the next flood. But she does not long remain unobserved. On a dumb barge, dropping down stream, is a lighterman, who, not content with his humble calling, evidently desires to be thought a humorist. He makes a gesture to indicate violent surprise, and then shouts out to a pal on the shore—

" Hi, Jim, 'ere's a bloomin' coffing with wings ! "

London.—At 10 p.m. the *Griffin* is under the shadow of St. Paul's. The darkness hides her curious build, and she threads her way, unobserved, among lighters and tugs. The river, in which is cast a hundred wriggling images of lamps upon the shore, or clusters of signal lights upon the railway bridges, is as impressive and as wonderful as any of the scenes through which the Toggenburg boat has passed, either in Switzerland, Germany, or Holland. London, viewed from the Thames at night, is like nothing else in the world.

Nov. Nearing Teddington, early morning.—While the sun is pushing its way through the layers of white fog that hang across the waters near Strawberry Vale, a figure may be seen slowly moving along the footpath towards Teddington. By the way he is leaning forward, and by the irregular movements of his shoulders it is evident that he is towing something, but a mast is at first all that can be seen above the mist. A nearer view, however, discloses a sailing-boat, in the stern of which another figure is seated at the helm. Not only is this craft of a build unknown to the upper reaches of the Thames, but her

TEDDINGTON.

condition is so extraordinary that a chance observer, seeing her glide into sight and silently vanish again into the fog, may be excused if he imagines that he has looked upon some ghostly and mysterious apparition from another world.

Her brown sails are furled, but not a few rents and ragged edges, rudely mended, show that there has been a hard struggle with the winds recently. Her hull is scarred and bruised from end to end. Its dark colour is tinted with every shade of green where the water-line is weed-covered, and bright patches of red lead here and there leap out in startling contrast. Her blunt bow, where it is shod with metal, is dinted and scraped and burnished, her rigging is knotted and spliced, and her lee-boards show signs of having been many times repaired.

Teddington, 8 *a.m.*—When the lock is reached, the mate hauls in the tow-rope and gets aboard, and the captain sculls from the stern towards the small gate. It is open, and the *Griffin* enters.

"She has seen some changes since she started," remarks the captain, as he looks affectionately at his much-battered boat. "I reckoned it out last night. Between Brunnadern and Teddington she has covered not far short of eight hundred miles."

Then the two men become aware that they are being regarded with curiosity by a man in an extraordinary hat. He is a boatman well known in

Teddington. At first his astonishment at the *Griffin* is quite overpowering; he is struck dumb. Never in the whole of his experience has he seen such a craft. The expression on his features is so ludicrous that, in spite of violent nudges from the mate, the captain can hardly restrain his laughter. At length, just as the *Griffin* is emerging from the upper gate, and is bidding good-bye to tidal waters, one concentrated exclamation reaches the ears of her crew : " Blowed if it ain't the Hark ! "

EPI-LOG

As the captain reclines in his hammock by the peaceful backwater, watching the smoke-rings from his cigarette and musing on the varied events of that pleasant autumn, nearly two years ago, he has but one regret ; and that is, that the *Griffin* lies at the bottom of the sea.

Yes, it is too true !

It happened in this way :—

Holiday time had come round again. Nature was calling to her children to come out and enjoy the sights that she had provided. The captain was not unheedful ; and, after balancing the claims of many rival plans, decided that the best thing he could do would be to take the *Griffin* once more across sea, with the object of cruising about the quaint canals and creeks of Holland.

On writing to the mate, he found, as luck would have it, that he also was free at the same time, and eagerly endorsed the plan ; so eagerly indeed, that the captain was tempted to suspect that his alacrity may not have been altogether unconnected with a certain magnetic attraction, to which allusion has been made. On being taxed with it, however, he vehemently repudiated the soft impeachment, and even went so far as to insinuate that the captain was only betraying his own motives by the remark.

At last it was mutually arranged that they should sail for Holland, but should on no account go near Veere, if it could possibly be avoided.

So the *Griffin* was re-fitted and started resplendent with new paint.

It boots not to dwell on the events of that short voyage ; suffice it to say that the weather was so bad (perhaps the reader remembers August of 1903) that all idea of crossing to Holland was abandoned, and most of the time was spent weathering gales off the Kentish coast. After a week of this, the captain and mate obtained a crew in the shape of a nautical friend, who, on account of his genuine knowledge of navigation, twice nearly wrecked the *Griffin*. It was soon apparent that seamanship of the ordinary kind was most misleading, and he finally surrendered attempts to manœuvre the boat to the two adventurers, whom he revered greatly as having adapted themselves to a unique and hitherto unknown system of sailing.

Everything went well until the great catastrophe on the afternoon of August 20th.

It was blowing hard from the S.S.E., and the *Griffin*, a few miles from the North Foreland, was working her way towards Broadstairs, through a very heavy sea streaked with foam. The mate had been pining all the afternoon for a cup of tea, but it was too rough to boil a kettle. The third member of the ship's company was even more fervent in his desire to get a civilized meal ashore. It was little wonder, therefore, that when the smack *H.C.B.*, bound for Ramsgate, came alongside and the captain declined a tow, there was almost a mutiny. He was at last persuaded to reverse his decision, and the smack was hailed.

No sooner had the *Griffin* been secured than her crew felt an irresistible desire to get on board the larger craft and stretch their legs. It was the second day that the *Griffin* had been out in the gale, and a night off Whitstable with three in the tiny cabin had not made matters easier.

Accordingly, the new hand scrambled on board the smack followed by the mate. The captain was the last to leave the ship, not, as he afterwards tried to maintain, out of a noble desire to stick to his post till the end, but because he wanted to finish some pears and cream, the consumption of which his duties "on the bridge" had temporarily interrupted.

The *H.C.B.*, a 22-ton boat, under double-reefed sails, was making a great pace through the rough water, with the *Griffin* flying along astern of her, when she rounded the Longnose and met the full force of the gale from the south-east. Then it became apparent that the boat in tow could not stand the high speed. She buried her nose in every wave and was pulled through by sheer force. In a minute it was all up with her, and she began to settle down. The *H.C.B.* was brought up into the wind and the *Griffin* hauled alongside, but there was a big sea running, so that, even if she could be held up, she would go to pieces against the smack.

The new hand, steadied by a rope round his waist, climbed down on to the cabin of the *Griffin*, and with an axe broke open the top and hauled out everything of value that was obtainable. These were passed up on to the deck of the fishing-boat, which was in a few moments strewn with sodden wearing apparel, cooking utensils, lamps, and rugs. But the sea was running high, and every moment the work became increasingly difficult, until it had to be abandoned altogether.

Then, one by one, the ropes were cast off, and the *Griffin* sank stern foremost into the seething waters.

And there she lies to this day, for aught that has been heard to the contrary, "full fathom five" off the Kentish coast, a source of astonishment, doubtless, alike to mermaids and to fishes, who in all their experience of wrecks have never seen the like of her before.

So, farewell to the *Griffin*. A short life and a merry one! Yet, after all, has she not fulfilled her purpose?

APPENDIX.

APPENDIX

SOMEWHERE concealed in " The Merchant Shipping Act of 1894 " there is a section numbered 567, under which it appears that the unfortunate master or owner (I am not quite clear which) of any craft wrecked upon the iron-bound coasts of Great Britain is liable to be mulcted of the sum of one pound sterling for his temerity.

To the uninitiated, the hazardous nature of the adventure might appear, like virtue, to be its own reward ; but the excellent framers of our laws evidently foresaw that unless some penalty were devised, our national existence might be imperilled by an over-indulgence of the inclination to become wrecked. With this in view they intelligently drafted section 567 of " The Merchant Shipping Act " of 1894.

Frankly, I have not read the Act itself, reserving it for some future time when I shall be at leisure to digest its wisdom; but as I have suffered under it, I feel it my bounden duty to warn all those who are likely to " go down to the sea in ships " and return without the ship, that to do so is a crime in the eyes of the law. To emphasise my words I append a reproduction of the receipt which was handed to me in return for my twenty shillings. The gravity of the crime is cunningly disguised, and the fine appears to have been extracted as a fee for allowing a wretched mariner to make a declaration, which as a matter of fact was dragged from his unwilling lips. To any one who contemplates becoming "a master of craft" I solemnly recommend "The Merchant Shipping Act of 1894," and would urge him to learn section 567 by heart, or place it in the form of an illuminated text in the cuddy.

Wr. 54.

Name of Ship.	Reference No. in Receiver's Report Book.
"Griffin"	87 03/04

Received from Mr. *D. Maxwell*

the sum of ___ *One* Pounds. ___

Shillings and ___ Pence, being the amount

of Fees and Expenses (as stated in the margin) due

under the 567th section of "The Merchant Shipping

Act, 1894," in respect of a Deposition taken by me re-

lating to the casualty to the Vessel *"Griffin"*

Dated at *Ramsgate*, the ___ 190

Scotlank Receiver.

Fee........£	1	:	:
Expenses...		:	:
Total £	1	:	:

CUSTOMS
21 AUG 1903
RAMSGATE

London: Printed for H. M. Stationery Office by Drake, Driver & Leaver, Ltd.

H.M. CUSTOMS' RECEIPT FOR £1.

4N

25ʳ Syd
1 Serv.